CALL ME SARAH

by

Lee Webber

Flip over for another great novel!
CAPERNAUM CENTURION

A BARBOUR BOOK

ISBN 1-55748-172-5

9 781557 481726

90000>

Printed in the United States of America

ISBN 1-55748-172-5

Typesetting by Typetronix, Inc.
Cape Coral, Florida

1

"Oh, Lord God of Israel, helper of the helpless, friend of the weak, come to my aid, I pray Thee! Save me from this fate that is about to befall me. Save me from this tragedy that awaits me when the sun rises in the east!"

Sarah lay on her straw mat and looked up into the dark blue Galilean night studded with a million stars. The night breeze stirred, and she drew around her the cloak that served as a coat by day and a blanket by night. If God did not answer her prayer, she would take this cloak, her only posession, when she was sold into slavery.

Sold into slavery! This should not happen to anyone, certainly not a daughter of Israel! The evil hand of poverty had reached out to strangle her family and rob her of any hope for the future.

Things had been hard, even before her mother had died. Things were hard for everyone in this little town of Ebba. No one really had enough to eat. Things were not much better even in Nazareth, some distance to the north. Then, since her mother had died, Sarah had to leave her childhood behind to take charge of the household chores, as well as help her father with the farming.

Although Sarah was only twelve, her sparkling dark eyes told everyone that she was not an ordinary girl, but one of perception beyond her years, with a quick wit and deep compassion. Her long black hair framed a pleasant face with regular features, smooth forehead, high cheekbones, and a rather small mouth. She was slightly taller than one would expect for a girl of her age. The long days of work in the field had made her strong, and the sun had made her brown as fine polished wood.

Her father's house was small, like most houses in Ebba, with walls of mud brick and floor simply of dirt pounded hard. The flat roof was made of branches plastered over with mud, and it had to be repaired frequently after heavy rain. No furniture needed to be polished, because there was none, except for a small, low table from which they ate. There was no real kitchen because cooking was done on a clay stove in the courtyard. When the weather was too bad for that, the stove had to be brought into the

1

house. Since there was no chimney, the house would fill with smoke, and the door, which swung on leather hinges, had to be left open so they could survive. A raised platform, about a cubit in height, was along one side of the room, and on this, the straw mats were laid out for sleeping. Often, especially in bad weather, the animals were brought into the house for the night — at least the chickens and goats. The scrawny donkey had to make do with a shelter of branches at the back of the house.

The small house and the lack of furniture did not mean that Sarah's workload was small. Every day, like the women of the village, she would rise at dawn. After washing in the courtyard — one could not wash in the house, not with a dirt floor — she would join them to get water from the town well. This was heavy work, but it was enjoyable because all the news of the village was shared at this time. The women kept a watchful eye on this little girl who so willingly took on the role of a woman and helped so much to keep her house going. "Dear little Sarah," said one of the older women, "she works so hard and you never hear her complain. Her father, Asher, he does not work as hard as she does! They are so far in debt to the overseer . . . well, we shall see."

By the time Sarah returned to the house, her father had washed, said his morning prayers, and was getting ready to go to his field, which was some distance from the house. In appearance, there was nothing extraordinary about Asher — medium height and average build, with strong shoulders and arms. His hair was long in the Jewish style, and his beard nicely trimmed. He looked like so many others. He was going to the field and would not be back until evening. So Sarah had prepared some barley bread on which she had poured a little olive oil, some onions, a piece of cheese, and a clay bottle, filled with half water, half wine. Before he left, Asher put his hands on Sarah's shoulders and said, "May the Lord bless you and keep you and give you joy in your labors in His sight this day." Sarah replied, "And may He make your crops to grow and ripen and fill your heart with joy."

After watching her father go, Sarah began the task of making bread. Without it, they could not live. A stone had been hollowed out to form a deep dish, and into this she poured the grain. With another stone, which fit into her hand, she ground it down into flour. She added salt and water and a piece of yeasted dough from the previous day. Then she kneaded it, put it in a clay bowl, and set it aside to rise. She gathered sticks to bake the bread, cared for the animals, and swept the dirt floor . . . the animals had been inside last night. Then she made the dough into small, flat cakes, built a fire in the clay stove, and baked the bread. When the task was done and all the loaves baked, she threw a pinch of flour into the oven; and, as the smoke ascended up to God, she said a prayer of thanksgiving for the food they had and a prayer on behalf of the hungry who had none. Next, she tended the small garden that would provide vegetables for the evening meal.

Sarah worked willingly and with joy. However, even as she did, she was aware of the fact that they were losing ground, and she knew why. Her mother was no longer here to encourage her father. Sarah remembered how her mother had gently encouraged Asher, guided him, even prodded him. "My lord Asher," she would say, "would this not be a good time to plow the field?"

"I have only one donkey, and I need two to plow. I'll have to wait until I can borrow another."

"At the well this morning," she would persist, "I heard Miriam say that her husband had finished plowing. Could you borrow one from him?"

"Perhaps I could . . . we will see."

Now that her mother was gone, the delays were longer, the harvests smaller. Sarah had done the best she could, but there were some things she could not do. She had to admit that her father was not a good farmer. Others would have their fields plowed, he would not; and he was the last to harvest, so that he lost a good deal of it. His field was small to begin with, and his mistakes meant that the harvest, which was meager to begin with, would be even smaller.

But there was another problem. If they could have kept all of the harvest, life would have been much easier. Of course, the first tenth went to the Lord, with praise and thanksgiving. Blessed be the name of the Lord! But then . . . how she remembered this!

It was the end of the barley harvest, and Sarah and her father had brought their sheaves to the town threshing floor. That was a happy time, a time of celebration when all the families gathered around to share the work and share the friendship. Around and around the ox dragged the threshing board, often with a child riding on it, not only for his own enjoyment, but also to add to the board to help separate the grain from the stalks more quickly. But the joy ended as soon as the threshing was done: Along came Simon the publican to collect the taxes for Rome, and he took one bushel out of four!

How Sarah despised that publican! "Look at him," she said under her breath. "That Babylonian robe he is wearing is worth more than our whole town! Look at the rings on his fingers; they must be worth a fortune! Look at his hair . . . not like a good decent Israelite; he has a 'Caesar' haircut, and no beard; he is trying to look like a Roman. And that superior look on his face. He thinks we are nothing but animals, as though we do not deserve to survive!''

Behind her, she heard a wife talking quietly to her husband. "This is not right!" she said in a tense whisper. "He is taking the food out of our children's mouths. Can't we do something about that?" Her husband sounded irritated in his reply, as though this had been the subject of discussion many times before without a resolution. "What do you expect us to do? Would you like to see us fight the Roman legions with ox-goads? Some things you can do, and some things you cannot do!"

"What we really need," said the wife, "is a deliverer."

Sarah listened to this, and a fire began to burn within her. For the first time, she felt the stirrings of righteous anger and feelings for her people as a nation, God's nation, which ought to be free. Then she said to herself almost aloud, *Queen Esther! yes, that's it.* Of course she knew well the story of Queen Esther, the girl who saved her nation. Each year at the feast of Purim, they celebrated this deliverance. "Why not me?" she asked. "God's deliverance can come from the most unlikely place. He can use little to accomplish much. Oh, God, why not me?"

There was murmuring and complaining in the crowd as the publican went about the task of hauling away his claimed taxes, but now Sarah was unaware of all of this. She stood in a cone of peace, closed her eyes, clenched her fists, and moved her lips silently as she prayed with all the fervor she could muster: "Oh, Lord, my God, make me like Queen Esther to avenge the wrongs done to my people Israel! Even if it costs me my life, let me strike a blow against the oppressors, against Rome. Let me help to prepare the way for our Messiah, who will deliver us and set us free!"

2

Sarah had prayed with deep faith and deep feeling, but that did not change the circumstances that surrounded her. In the days that followed, her father would often look at his daughter and wonder what was to become of her if he failed. Then he would resolve to work harder, to be more diligent, never to be late in planting, never to be late in reaping. He had been late last year; and, as a result, much of the grain had fallen to the ground and was lost. No, he would never let that happen again. But then discouragement would set in. "No matter how hard I work, I can never climb out of this black hole of poverty. I cannot raise enough for us to eat; how can I ever pay back what I have had to borrow over the years?"

At times Sarah could see the despair in his eyes, and she heard him tossing on his mat at night. She wanted to talk to him about this, but could not find the words; and, since he remained silent, she remained silent. She did not know what else to do.

One bright, sunny day, most of the townspeople were gathered around the threshing floor when a visitor appeared. He looked like a wild man: hair uncombed, a long beard that evidently had not been tended for a long time, and a rough, camel hair robe fastened with a wide leather belt hung loosely on his gaunt, angular frame. His sandals appeared to be nothing more than rough pieces of leather with thongs wrapped around his legs to his knees.

Zadok, the elder of the village, was seated on the bench watching him approach. Zadok certainly looked the part of a town elder: white hair, white beard, white robe with a mantle thrown over his shoulders. Dark, flashing eyes seemed to take in and understand fully all that went on around him. In spite of his age, he held himself erect, but now he leaned over to speak quietly to the man seated beside him.

The man, whose name was Abner, looked young enough to be his son. He was not, but it was evident that there was a bond between them — the bond between a disciple and his teacher. Indeed, it was Zadok's intention to impart as much knowledge as possible to this young man who held such promise.

"Do you see that man approaching?" Zadok was saying, "He comes from the northern hills of Galilee and is a member of a band of radicals. They call themselves Nationalists, and I suppose they are; but Rome calls them revolutionaries, and they are that too. They perceive themselves to be the only true Israelites, the only ones with vision and courage. I am sure that he is going from town to town to get recruits. He would like to be the leader of a rebellion. Yes, I know him; his name is Reuben and he comes from Nazareth. He will probably want to give his oration here to the people."

"What will you do about it?" asked Abner.

"We don't need that kind of trouble here, but I will let him speak. I would rather have this out in the open, not behind closed doors. What he says is very convincing, and it is something the people are thinking about, so we will have to deal with it."

As the stranger walked into the crowd, he looked around and then asked loudly, "Who is the elder of this village?" The people became silent, all watching to see what was going to happen. Several people pointed to Zadok, who sat still, watching. The stranger walked over to him and said, "I am Elijah, and I have come on a mission."

"I know who you are," said Zadok, "and you are not Elijah; you are Reuben from Nazareth. Nevertheless, what do you want here in Ebba?"

"I wish to talk to the people about the hope of Israel; surely you cannot deny me that opportunity."

"No, I cannot," replied Zadok. "I am well aware of our problems as a nation, and we are not friends of Rome here, but I want you to know that *I* will make the final decision here. Go ahead and speak."

The stranger took a few steps ahead and stood looking at the crowd. Then he raised his arms and said loudly, "I am Elijah . . ." He paused as he remembered what Zadok had said to him, and then continued, "That is to say, just as Elijah came from the hill country to confront the evil King Ahab in the name of the Lord, even so I come from the hills to say that the days of the evil King Herod, and indeed, the days of our enslavement to Rome are about to come to an end. I proclaim this to you in the name of the Lord!"

Zadok stood up slowly, raising his hand, and said, "It is easy to say, 'I proclaim this in the name of the Lord.' Many propose to speak for Him, and many of the things they proclaim never come to pass. The things that do come to pass will tell us whether you speak in the name of the Lord, or not."

"What I shall speak, you know to be true, and the people will know it, too. These things must be spoken, and they must be heard! A voice needs to cry out! This evil must not go unchallenged!" He paused and looked around at the people with piercing eyes, seeking to rivet all their attention on himself.

Then he began his oration.

"Herod calls himself King of the Jews, but who made him king? Did anyone ask you? Did you say, 'Come, be our king; you are a good and righteous man'? No, you did not! You would never ask him to be your king. He is not a true Israelite. He is an Edomite! Then, who made him king? The Roman emperor did! And why? I will tell you why — to enslave us all, to tax us to death, and to take away our identity as God's holy nation!"

He said this with great force, one might say with vehemence, rocking back and forth, rising on his toes, waving his arms for emphasis. He paused to catch his breath and then called out, "Is this not true?"

From the back of the crowd, one of the younger men shouted, "Amen! It is true! You are right!" With this encouragement, he continued.

"And what has this so-called king done to our holy city, Jerusalem, the gem of all the earth, the joy of God Himself? What has he done?" He paused as though he were asking for a reply, and the crowd waited with anticipation. With a low voice, almost a whisper, he said, "This king . . . this king" — saying the word *king* with a sneer — "this king" — he took a deep breath and then shouted — "has violated, has polluted, has desecrated the city of God! Is this not true?"

This time the response was much more enthusiastic. Some shouted, some raised their arms, some nodded their heads.

"This king," he continued, "has filled Jerusalem with heathen spectacles of Rome, and in his amphitheater the contestants in the games perform naked! Would a true king of Israel do this?"

"No, no!" shouted the crowd.

"And he built a lavish theater covered with gold and silver and precious stones, all paid for by your taxes; and in this theater, all kinds of immorality and debauchery are paraded before the eyes of the ungodly audience. Would a true king of Israel do that?"

"No, no, no!"

"And how many wives has he had? One? Two? Three? Oh, no! You can hardly count them on the fingers of your two hands. And how many children has he sired? Who can count them? And how many has he murdered? He has murdered not only his enemies, but his wives and children, and blood flows like water wherever this monster treads! Would the true king of Israel do this?"

"No, no, no!"

He waited for a long moment, then held up his hands, and, after a prolonged silence, said, "And what do you, the good people of Ebba, do about this? You do nothing! Oh, yes, you complain among yourselves, but when the publican comes, you pay and pay, like lambs led to the slaughter. You say nothing while Rome robs you of the grain that should go to feed your children. You should act . . . you *must* act! I have made my decision; I would rather die than submit to this indignity!''

He finished his oration and stood aside to await the reply which he expected would be favorable because of his overwhelming reasoning and fervor.

"And you will die," said Zadok quietly, as he rose to his feet. "You will die soon enough if Rome hears you talk like this. We are true Israelites, as much as you are, but we cannot run to the hills and hide in the caves as you do when the Romans come. We have wives and little ones, and we must think of them. If we withheld our taxes, that would be the end of all of us. No, you cannot fight the legions of Rome with a few sticks and spears. It will take more than that! It will take the hand of God; it will take a deliverer sent by Him. He has done this in the past when we were downtrodden. He did it by the hand of Gideon; He did it by the hand of David when he was but a lad; He even did it by a young girl, Queen Esther. And one day — and I pray that it will be soon — one day He will do it once and for all by the hand of the Messiah.''

Sarah heard no more: Zadok had said *Esther*. Her heart was pounding. That was exactly what she had prayed for when she first felt this stirring! This seemed like the voice of God to her. Again she closed her eyes and prayed, "Oh, Lord, make me like Esther so I may deliver my people!''

One day, Asher was plowing his wheat field with his wooden plow which was little more than a crooked stick to which he had attached an iron point. It turned over so little earth that he could plow only half an acre of ground during a hard day's labor. Two scrawny donkeys struggled against the pull of the plow; they seemed to stagger ahead rather than pull with strength. Asher had his tunic pulled up and tucked into his belt to free his legs as he struggled behind the animals, right hand on the plow, a stick in the left to direct the progress of the team. At the end of a row, he halted, wiped the sweat from his brow, and looked up at the sun. *It must be midday,* he thought. *One more pass and I will sit for a while under the tree and take care of my thirst.*

"Asher, Asher!" Someone was calling him. Who could it be? He turned to see, and immediately recognized the man approaching him. His heart fell. It was his overseer, and this could not be good news. The overseer, whose name was Solomon, was a large man with bushy eyebrows and graying hair around the temples. True, he worked for the Romans — in fact this land was owned by King Herod — but all admitted that Solomon was fair and honest, and this was rare. Many overseers made themselves rich at the expense of the farmers. Asher liked Solomon because he had been kind enough to lend him seed grain to keep him going. Nevertheless, he was not glad to see Solomon; he had never come to the field before, and Asher knew that this meant trouble.

Solomon drew closer and called to Asher, "Asher, come sit under the tree for a few minutes. I need to talk to you."

Asher set the plow on the ground and, with hesitant step, went to meet Solomon. He walked a few paces behind as they headed for the shade of the tree; he was not anxious to start any conversation, for he knew what was going to be said. Solomon began. "Has the Lord been smiling upon you, Asher?"

Asher thought to himself, *Yes, Solomon is a kind man; he is trying to make this as easy for me as possible, and I am thankful for that.* So he replied, "Yes, Solomon, God has been good; and to you?"

"Oh, yes, Asher, God is good." Solomon paused, looking for the right words to begin, looking, but not able to find them. Then he said, "Asher . . ." Once more he paused, then he swallowed, cleared his throat, and began again. "Asher, you know that I am just the overseer; I cannot do as I wish. Many, many times I must do what I do not wish to do, as now."

Asher shifted uneasily and looked across the field. He said nothing but waited for Solomon to continue. After a moment or two, he did.

"The king's treasurer came from Jerusalem to look over my books. Carefully he went over each account, calculating, checking, nodding. Then he came to your account. 'What is this, Solomon?' he asked. I said nothing; what could I say? Then he went on, 'Each year this man goes deeper into debt; he is not keeping even. The more you lend him, the worse his conditon becomes. We cannot let this go on. If I closed my eyes to this, I would be called to account for it. What do you plan to do about it?' Asher, what could I say?"

Solomon paused again, then looked away. Asher could see that this was painful for him. After a moment he went on. "Asher, I am going to take you into servitude until your debt is paid. Face it, you are not a good farmer; you will work better under a manager. You wouldn't have to work any harder than you do now on this small plot of ground, and you would get more to eat. In a few years, you would have your freedom, if you care to take it, but you might be content to stay under the master. What do you think?"

Asher's mind was in turmoil. This did not come as a surprise — he had been expecting it for a long time — but still he had no reply. No matter how he looked at it, he seemed to have no choice. Then he asked, "And what about my daughter, Sarah? Could I bring her with me?"

Solomon had been anticipating this question; and, if Asher had not asked it, he would have had to bring it up. This was the hardest part. "That's the problem. We do not need another maid. I talked with the treasurer about this and explained your situation, but he said, at this time, he could not justify taking on another girl. He promised me that he would find a good place for her, where she would be treated kindly and have a good place to work. I am sorry about this, but when you think of it, it may be best for her. She has had to work too hard."

Solomon was satisfied that he had made the best case possible for this difficult situation, and he was beginning to hope that it would have a pleasant conclusion after all.

Asher frowned, shifted his feet, smoothed the dirt on which they sat, and appeared to be deep in thought. Actually, he was trapped. He recognized the fact that, although Solomon was giving him a choice, in reality, he had no choice, but he had to try. "No, I couldn't go without Sarah," he said, trying to sound firm and convincing, as though this were the line he would not cross. Perhaps his firmness could change the decision. "No, I couldn't do it."

"I thought you would say that," responded Solomon, "and I told the treasurer that would be your reply. I asked for a little time. I reminded him that I had already lent you wheat for seed, and I suggested that we wait until after the wheat harvest to decide. He was willing to agree to this, but if the harvest is not enough to begin paying back the debt in a substantial manner, we will have to go through with the arrangements as planned."

Solomon stood up, adjusted his robe, gave his hand to Asher to help him up, and said, "For your sake, Asher, I shall pray that the Lord will give you a bountiful harvest, the best you have ever known." Without saying more, he turned and left.

Asher just stood there watching him go. He knew how hard this had been for Solomon; he could see the emotions of sadness and pity in his eyes. Solomon had done all he could, and Asher was grateful to him; but the fact remained that his future and especially the future of his daughter were very much in doubt.

Slowly he walked across the field, picked up the plow, tapped the donkeys with the switch, and started down the row. As the plow dug into the earth, he began to think; and, since he was alone, he began to speak out loud: "This is not good! Last year, I got only four bushels of grain for each bushel of seed. I gladly give the Lord His tenth. Unwillingly I give Rome one bushel out of four. I have to pay the rent on the land. I have to repay the seed grain . . . but if I do that, I have nothing to eat, and no seed for next year. What can I do?"

Asher decided he would say nothing to Sarah. It would only worry her, and there was nothing she could do about it. But Sarah knew something was wrong. A number of times she was about to ask him about it, but hesitated. If her father wanted to tell her about it, he would speak; if he did not wish to speak, she would not pry.

Asher tried to do the best job he could. He plowed carefully, making sure that all rocks were removed and all thistles dug out. Then he broadcast the seed, carefully measuring each stride to match the circle of the falling grain, not too much in one place, no places missed. Then he plowed across the furrows to cover the seed; and, as an added precaution, he used a branch to try to cover any seed that remained in sight. He was not entirely successful, as he soon learned when the birds appeared; the birds did not go away empty. "I have done the best I could," he said, already sensing defeat. "Now all I can do is trust the Lord for the harvest."

The wheat harvest drew near. One morning, when it came time for Asher to leave for the field, he hesitated, reluctant to go. This puzzled Sarah because she knew how important it was for the field to be tended. It seemed as though her father had lost interest. "My father," she said, "could I come and help you in the field today?" She thought that perhaps her companionship would encourage him, and she determined to work as hard as possible to keep things going. Asher did not seem excited about her offer, but he did not feel that he could refuse. So he said, "If you like," and they went to the field together.

Sarah was surprised to see how many weeds were growing with the wheat. To hide her surprise, she said, "Is it not strange that the weeds grow so well without care, and the wheat grows so poorly no matter how much care is lavished upon it?" She said it with a cheerful voice to lighten her father's heart, but also because she could sense his embarrassment at a field so poorly cared for. "You start at one end of the field, and I will start at the other, and we will meet in the middle," said Sarah, and off she went to the far end of the field to begin her work. In a short time, Asher heard her singing a song that she was making up as she went:

> "Out, out weeds; grow, grow wheat.
> Come rain; come sun.
> Lord, give us a good harvest."

It almost broke Asher's heart; the harvest again was going to be poor. Nothing could hold back the calamity that was about to engulf them.

One morning, not long after that, Sarah started out to go to the well for water. Before she got to the door, she overheard two women who were several paces ahead of her. "Isn't it a shame about Asher and poor little Sarah! Asher goes into servitude because of his debts, and Sarah is going to be sold as a slave!"

Horrified, Sarah stepped back into the house. Her father was adjusting his belt and putting on his sandals. "Father," she cried with fear in her voice and tears in her eyes, "what is going to happen to me?"

"My daughter," said Asher, turning aside so she could not see the tears in his eyes. "My daughter, we must trust in God who is our provider. He will not fail us. Now, go; get the water."

That night Sarah climbed the ladder leaning against the side of the house and went up to the roof to sleep. Often, in good weather it was more pleasant to sleep on the roof than in the small, dark house. As she climbed, she wondered if she would ever do this again. Where would she sleep tomorrow night? This night especially, this night above all nights, she had to sleep on the roof, because her main occupation was to pray. No walls, no roof should stand in the way of her prayers ascending up to God.

She searched the heavens, wondering what far-off spot could be the location of God's heavenly home. If only she could bow before God and present her petition; surely she could touch His great heart of love. So she prayed: "Oh, Lord God of Israel, helper of the helpless, friend of the weak, come to my aid, I pray Thee. Save me from this fate that is about to befall me, from this tragedy that awaits me when the sun rises in the east. Oh, Lord, You know I have given my life to You. Oh, how I have prayed that You would make me like Queen Esther to save and deliver my people. But I am not like Esther; I cannot even save my own family; I cannot even save myself. I am not Esther; I am only Sarah."

The morning came, and there was no help in sight, no answer to her fervent prayers. How empty and depressing the house seemed in the morning gloom. How sad it was to leave the only house she had ever known, and to leave for an unknown future.

They left the village and started out. They were to meet a servant where the road divided; he would conduct Sarah on the road south to meet a caravan. Asher would take the road north. As they walked, Asher told his daughter, "Do not look back; your life is not back there any longer. Look ahead!"

"I am trying to do that," replied Sarah. "But I can see nothing ahead of me but clouds of uncertainty."

"No one knows the future but God," said Asher, "and He does not choose to reveal it to us. We must trust and walk in the path He shows us."

Most of the time they walked in silence, both of them deep in thought. Neither was able or willing to share the doubts and fears they faced. Eventually they came to the place where the road divided. There, seated beside the road, they saw the servant from the master's house. As they came nearer, he rose and greeted them. "You must be Asher," he said, "and this must be Sarah. I have been sent to be her guide."

"Where will she be going?" asked Asher, his voice trembling with emotion and fear.

"I do not know," said the servant. "I have been given orders to take her to meet a trader named Benazra on the road to Jerusalem; that's all I know."

This was not happy news, but there was no appeal, no person to reason with, no way to change the decision. It was out of their hands now. Sarah's worst fears were realized. Asher said to the servant, "Give us a few moments to say good-bye; we won't be long."

"Most gladly," said the servant, who then turned his back and walked a way down the road. He did not wish to witness such a scene of sadness.

For a little while, they stood in silence, and then Asher spoke. "Oh, Sarah, my dear daughter, how this parting pains me and wounds my heart. Most of all, I grieve because I have not been a good father to you."

Sarah quickly interrupted Asher, hugging him tight, and said, "Yes you have, you *have* been a good father to me! Please don't say that."

"No," Asher insisted, "I haven't. Since your mother died, I have been too silent, too locked up within myself. Many times I wanted to speak and build a bond between us, but the words would not come. I was a silent man, living within my own shell. I was lonely, but I knew you were lonely, too. I have failed you when you needed me most."

Sarah was weeping now and saying between sobs. "No father, no father; that is not true."

But Asher did not seem to hear. There were some things he had been thinking about for a long time, things that weighed heavily on his guilty conscience, things he had to say before they parted. He went on, "I have not been a diligent farmer, and my laziness has cost both of us our futures. I would promise myself that I would do better, work harder, but somehow that never happened. Perhaps I do need a master over me to tell me what to do and when to do it. But what a price I pay for my laziness! I say good-bye to you now, and I wonder if I shall ever see you again! What have I done to you? Most gladly would I work myself down to an early grave if I could save you and keep you with me, but I do not have that choice. I must trust the overseer who tells me you will be better off where you are going. But I do not know where! And you will be all alone! This breaks my heart, and I can do nothing about it. I pray that God will forgive me, and I beg you to forgive me and think kindly of me.''

Sarah clung to her father. Both of them were weeping. Neither could speak. Suddenly, Asher kissed her on the forehead, turned, and started on the road north. His loud sobbing could be heard as he walked with stooped shoulders and weary tread.

He did not look back.

3

When Sarah and the servant came to the road that led south, they found a caravan waiting for them. The servant who had brought Sarah went up to the man who seemed to be in charge and began talking to him. Sarah stood to one side, waiting, fearful, terrified. Her headdress was drawn tightly across her face so that only her eyes were visible. They were red and puffy from crying. She watched as the servant gave a scroll to the trader and money was exchanged.

"Sure enough," she said to herself, "I have been sold!"

After a brief conversation, the servant turned and started to leave. Sarah did not even know his name; there had been no conversation during the journey. She had walked several paces behind him. It was obvious that this assignment was distasteful to him, and certainly Sarah had no desire to speak. As he left, however, Sarah felt that she had lost the last tie to the life she had known; the last thread had been broken. Now she was adrift on an unknown sea.

The trader, whose name was Benazra, came to Sarah and asked gently, "What is your name?" Sarah replied in a low, muffled voice that he had to ask again. When he heard her name he said, "Now, girl, we have to come to an understanding. You have to understand, first of all, that I am in no way responsible for what has happened to you. I am a kind man, I am a trader. I am not a slave trader. But let me make this clear: It is my job to get you to Jerusalem, and I am going to do it. If you want to do it the hard way, that's your choice; I will tie you like a sack of grain and put you on the back of a camel. This will be unpleasant. Your other option is to promise me that you will do what I tell you, and you can have a pleasant journey. Now, what is your choice?"

"I choose to obey," replied Sarah quietly.

"Have you ever ridden a camel?" asked Benazra. But before Sarah could answer, he said, "I suppose that is a foolish question. Well, let me tell you that this is not a good time to start. I know walking may seem hard, but a camel is not a comfortable beast to ride. It is an awkward animal which

15

moves both legs on one side and then both legs on the other side, and you will be pitched from side to side like a small ship on the sea. It is true that we need the space for cargo, but I don't want you to think I have no conscience just because I make you walk. You will notice that I walk, too. Now do we have an understanding? Will you behave?''

"Yes," replied Sarah, "I promise that I will be no problem."

"My drivers have been with me for years. They are all good men and they will help you. That man," said Benazra as he pointed to a young fellow who appeared to be about eighteen, "he is also a slave going to Jerusalem. Now, let's get moving. We must make it to Caesarea by nightfall." With this, he went to the head of the caravan of five camels, and they started off.

So this is the way my new life begins, thought Sarah. There was something about Benazra's forthrightness that put her mind at peace; she looked at him now as her protector.

Benazra was a sturdy man, with short legs; if his legs had been in proportion to the rest of his body, he would have been a tall man. His shoulders and arms were strong, as though he had done a lot of heavy lifting. That, indeed, was true; he had spent most of his life loading and unloading camels. Although he was from Damascus, he was a Jew, not a Syrian. His father had been a carpenter in Damascus, an energetic, imaginative man who saw the possibilities in change rather than the difficulties it presented.

The world Benazra's father saw was changing. The Roman armies brought Roman law and a form of peace to fragmented, warring nations. Indeed, Caesar Augustus was determined that there would be peace over all the earth. He also determined that he, personally, would visit every province of the far-flung empire. He would require roads and a vast army that could build the roads as they spread the peace. And the roads would be built to last. It would not be enough to level the ground and lay a few stones; these roads would be built for the centuries, and they would all lead to Rome. Benazra's father saw the new roads and the new safety and decided that there was more money to be made in trading than in carpentering, so he bought a few camels and started out. The changes had opened up a new life for him, and from that beginning had come the trading empire now run by Benazra.

He was now a wealthy man, though one would never know it by looking at him; he was dressed as any ordinary Jew would dress. One would not expect him to be on caravan, either, but it was in his blood, and he enjoyed the life. He liked to keep up with his business contacts personally.

The caravan looked like any other ordinary caravan, but it was not. The cargo camouflaged in the worn saddlebags was precious. They had a large quantity of silk from far-off China, worth its weight in gold. In fact, it actually was often paid for that way, pound for pound. They had pepper and spices from India, and these were rare indeed. In Tyre, Benazra had loaded on purple dye made from a shellfish, and, consequently, so rare and costly that it was normally limited to royalty. However, he had many customers for it in Jerusalem, not only in Herod's palace, but among the many aristocrats who gathered around him. This would be a profitable trip.

Sarah walked beside one of the camels. She did not have a hard time keeping up, but the pace was steady, and she was sure that she would be ready to sleep when the time came.

After several hours of walking, she found herself alongside of the young man Benazra had pointed out. She did not realize that she had slowed down, or else that he had quickened his pace, but now they were side by side. When Sarah realized this, she was embarrassed and looked away, but she could not avoid him when he spoke. "My name is Alex," he said. "What is your name?"

Sarah said nothing, partly because of modesty, partly because of fear of strangers, but mostly because he appeared to be a Gentile. Alex walked along quietly for a long time saying nothing, sensing her pain and fear. Then he said, "We should talk; we need to help each other. It is not good to face your problems alone; you need a friend." Still Sarah said nothing. Rather than responding, she quickened her pace, and Alex dropped behind.

Benazra watched her and wondered what he should do. He felt sorry for this girl, so rudely uprooted from her home, going to such an uncertain future. He was a compassionate man and wished he could find a way to mitigate her sorrow, but it seemed she had already withdrawn into her shell, hoping to shut out reality by shutting out the things around her. "Perhaps I should talk to her," he said, as he watched her walk, head down, lost in the sorrow of her situation. They were nearing the city of Caesarea, and Benazra was anxious to see the reaction this village girl would have when this magnificent city came into view. Many times in the past as he journeyed down this road, he had watched in amazement as he saw this city in the process of construction. It had taken twelve years to build and the marvel of this great labor was evident. *This sight should be enough,* he thought, *to stir her out of her lethargy and restore her interest in life. At least it is worth a try.* So he went back to walk with Sarah. Indeed, the story of Caesarea had more impact than he had expected.

When they came to a rise in the road, the city lay spread out before them, its harbor reaching out into the Great Sea, with blue waters as far as the eye could see.

"Look!" said Benazra, raising his arm and motioning toward the panorama spread before them. "Have you ever seen anything as beautiful as that?" Sarah lifted her eyes reluctantly and looked; then she looked again. What she saw, she could not believe. A girl from a tiny, obscure village could not be expected to imagine such a city! It was made of marble with high walls, imposing buildings, and a harbor almost completely enclosed, so that even the huge ships floated on a sea of glass, a private pool. A tall lighthouse dominated the harbor at the far end of the breakwater. The four sides of the breakwater were decorated with six enormous statues set on six high pillars.

"I came by here as they were laying the foundations for the breakwater in the midst of the sea," Benazra said. "I saw the stones that they brought to set on the seafloor for the foundations. A man could take more than fifteen strides on the top of them; a man standing on the ground could not reach the top. This harbor is larger than the one in Athens, and those ships you see there are the largest in the world. They come, not only from Rome, but from Spain and Britain. But, see that great marble temple just in front of the harbor? That is the temple to Caesar Augustus; King Herod, who built this city, named it after him and dedicated it to him. Inside is one of the largest images of Caesar in the world, and there is another, equally as large, of the goddess Roma."

Sarah looked at him with shock . . . images in the temple? No, that could not be! Then she said, "But surely King Herod, King of the Jews, would not build a temple with heathen images!"

"Oh, Sarah, how naive you are," said Benazra. "You are going to find that the world is not as you imagined when you were back in your hometown; and it is not as it should be. Do you know how Herod became King of the Jews? When the Roman senate gave him the title, he went to the heathen temple in Rome with Mark Anthony on his left and Caesar Augustus on his right and offered sacrifices to Jupiter, Juno, and Minerva. That's how we got our King of the Jews!"

"No Jew would offer sacrifices in a heathen temple. No Jew would even enter a heathen temple. He would rather die than do that! You must be wrong!" said Sarah in a voice trembling with emotion.

"No Sarah, I am sorry to say that is the truth about our king," said Benazra. "But now look; see that large amphitheater over there? That's where they held the Olympic Games and King Herod was the leader."

"Then the man was right; the man was right!" shouted Sarah.

"What man was right?" asked Benazra.

"There was a man who called himself Elijah who came to our village and told us some things about King Herod, and he told us that Herod even holds heathen games in the Holy City.'' Then Sarah stood still and said with firmness and conviction, "He is not the true king of our people; he is the enemy of our people."

Benazra saw how stirred Sarah was, and so he said, "Sarah, you should not trouble yourself about this. There is nothing you can do about it. Leave that to others who are wiser and stronger than you are."

But Sarah was not listening.

4

Just outside the city, where the road turned to the south, the travelers came to the inn where they would spend the night. A good inn in a good location made money for the owner. Roman roads had many inns like this one, spaced a day's journey apart. It was surrounded by a high wall, with a gate just high enough and wide enough to allow a loaded camel to enter. When night came, this gate was closed, and the people and animals inside were relatively safe. The inn was mostly a courtyard with stalls for the animals on the side; and, above the stalls on the second floor, were rooms for the travelers who could afford them. The rest, who could not, rolled out their mats and slept in the yard.

Benazra led his caravan through the gate and then went to make arrangements with the innkeeper. He asked for food and water for the camels and supper for his party. The next day he would need food for the journey. He also made arrangements for a room for himself upstairs; the rest would sleep in the courtyard. The camels were unloaded and the merchandise carefully piled near the wall in the far corner. After the camels had been cared for, the travelers sat down to supper.

The meal for that night was lamb stew, and the travelers sat around a common pot into which they dipped pieces of bread. At first, Sarah thought she would not eat. Benazra watched her closely, but said nothing. She would need food and rest for the journey on the following day. "Here, Sarah, try this," said Benazra, as he dipped a piece of bread into the stew and brought up a piece of tender lamb. Sarah hesitated briefly, but in order to be polite, she took the bread and ate it. After the first few bites, she changed her mind; she was hungry! Perhaps it was the long walk; perhaps it was the fact that the worry of the past few days had taken away her appetite so that she had not eaten a real meal for several days. Whatever it was, when she began to eat, she thought that she had never tasted such delicious food in her life. She ate her share. Benazra smiled to himself and thought, *That girl is a survivor; she will manage whatever comes her way.*

Soon after supper, Sarah took her mat and found a place near the corner of the wall to call her own. As she lay on the mat, she looked up into the same Galilean sky into which she had sent her prayers the previous night, and she began to consider all the things that had happened to her that day. She wondered where her father was, and she wished that she had some way to communicate to him that she had not been overwhelmed by the events of the day. Then she prayed: "Oh, Lord, I have dreaded this day more than I have dreaded any day of my life; but here I am, with the night sky over me, and Your mercy has kept me every step of my journey. What tomorrow holds, I do not know; but, as I have trusted You for today, so I will trust for tomorrow and the days to come."

After she had prayed she thought, *How strange it is; I am more at peace in this foreign place than I was last night on my own rooftop. The uncertainty was worse than reality. I will try to remember that.*

Even though she was tired, Sarah found that sleep did not come easily. There was still commotion in the courtyard, especially from three strangers seated around a charcoal fire burning in a flat, round metal dish. They were passing a wineskin among them, and it was obvious that the wine was having an effect on them. The conversation became louder and more animated. The largest of the three, a burly man with rolls of fat around his neck and waist, noticed Alex watching them with obvious disgust. The man, face florid with wine, eyes bulging, called out to him, "Hey, you over there! Come have a drink with us."

"No, thank you," said Alex, trying to hide his animosity. But the man would not let it go at that; he was clearly seeking a confrontation. Then he said, quite loudly, "I saw you come in with a girl. Bring her over here, and let's be friends." When Sarah heard that, she stiffened, terrified, and tried to hide herself in the shadows.

"The girl doesn't want to come over there," Alex said brusquely. "She is tired and wants to sleep." This angered the man even more, and he said, "Who gave you the right to speak for her? I want to hear it from her; maybe she does."

Sarah did not hear anymore. She knew that a storm was rising and about to engulf her. Then she saw the big man pull a knife from under his robe and begin to stagger toward her. In one swift move, Alex lifted Sarah to her feet, pushed her to the wall, and covered her body with his own. But his hands were empty; he was no match for the attacker.

All at once, a voice of authority rang out, "You there . . . with the knife! Stop where you are!" It was the innkeeper, who had been aroused by the disturbance in the courtyard. "Go back where you belong, or I am going to throw you out and call the Roman soldiers!''

The man was drunk, no doubt, but he stopped in his tracks, startled by this voice that came from above, like a voice out of heaven. He turned to locate the source of the voice, but in the darkness, he could not. Mumbling to himself, he retreated to his place and sat down heavily. The innkeeper gave a final exhortation and then retreated to his room. Soon things became quiet.

Sarah was so shaken that she could not speak; she could not even manage to mumble, ''Thank you.'' She slumped down on her mat in silence. As she lay on her cot which, only a few moments ago, had been her meeting place with God, she wondered aloud, ''What kind of a world is this? How can these things happen?'' It took her a long time to fall asleep.

It was hardly dawn when things began to stir in the courtyard. One man was loading his camel, and the beast was protesting so loudly one would think it was being abused badly. This was normal behavior for camels; but once loaded, they seemed to bear their heavy burdens patiently, and they could go twenty miles a day without much complaint. The noise of the camel awakened Sarah. She had found a nook behind one of the saddlebags next to the wall; and, in spite of the incident the preceding night, she felt quite safe there and, to her surprise, had slept well.

It was time now for washing and morning prayer. Instead of pouring water on her hands outside her front door as she had always done, this country girl found that the inn had running water, and something she had never heard of: a city sewer connection. One amazement after another left her wide-eyed with wonder and taught her quickly that the world she was entering was a far cry from the primitive life she had known. Her village life had remained unchanged for centuries; now she was brought face-to-face with conveniences and customs she did not know even existed.

Benazra had gone into Caesarea with one of the camels for some special business and was just returning as Sarah rolled up her mat. ''And how is my traveler this day?'' he asked in a cheerful voice. ''Has God been with you through the night?''

''Thanks be to God,'' responded Sarah. ''His protection has been over me, and His mercies are new every morning.'' She wondered if Benazra knew about the frightening incident of the previous night, but she decided that if he did not mention it neither would she.

One of the camel drivers brought breakfast, consisting of bread, cheese, and dates; and, after Benazra said a prayer of thanksgiving to God, they began to eat. Sarah wondered what Alex would think of this since he was a foreigner, whether he was uncomfortable about it or would simply choose to ignore it. She did not look at him to see his reaction. In fact, she had avoided him because she did not know how to react to him. The men drank wine and poured some in a dish, and into this, they dipped the bread to make it a more palatable breakfast. Sarah had camel's milk that had been mixed with three parts water. After breakfast the camels were loaded, and they went out of the gate and headed south.

The inn at Caesarea was situated, perhaps on purpose, next to the parade grounds of the Roman garrison. As they came out of the inn, she saw row after row of Roman cavalrymen mounted on magnificent horses, all lined up in parade position. Each man wore the traditional Roman helmet, armor, and short Roman sword. Beyond the cavalry, the legions were formed with a centurion and his banners at the head of each hundred. There appeared to be thousands of them.

"This is the army of occupation!" Sarah grumbled.

"Yes, indeed it is," replied Benazra, "but remember this: It is also the army that has built this road on which we travel to Jerusalem and has made it safe for us to travel. My business has thrived because of their umbrella of protection. But you are right; our taxes have paid for it all."

"Yes," said Sarah, "and the grain we raised has gone to feed that army, and I travel this fine road to Jerusalem against my will, because the taxes have forced us into poverty. Look at this beautiful city: I do not enjoy it! What good does it do me? Shall I ever see it again? I have been robbed of my home, my father, to pay for this," she said vehemently.

"You sound like a revolutionary!" said Benazra. "If I were you, I wouldn't talk like that too loudly. Let me give you a little advice: When you get to Jerusalem, be very careful to whom you talk like this, or your life will be shorter than you think. There are many in Jerusalem who feel as you do, but they are all in danger. Remember what you see before you now, and remember that this is only a small part of the might of Rome, and Rome will use that might ruthlessly to put down any insurrection."

Benazra paused to make sure that Sarah heard his warning, giving it time to sink in; and then, surprisingly, he added, "But if I were younger, perhaps I would join you."

Benazra could never know what this last word did for Sarah; it lit the fire again! It seemed as though, every time she was tempted to think that she would be of no use in the struggle against oppression, someone would come along to fan the embers, and the passion would burn again. Perhaps she *was* to be an Esther!

5

The day settled down to the routine, walking, walking, walking. Sarah was walking, but she was also reconsidering this young man who had placed himself as a shield between herself and the danger that had threatened her last night. What should she do? She could hardly avoid him! No, she should not avoid him. At the very least, she would thank him for his courageous, generous act. She debated for a long time, thinking she would go back and thank him, but she could never muster up the courage. As she was thinking about this, she turned to see where he was and was surprised to see that he was just behind her. She turned to him and said, "You are a Gentile?" It was a question, but a statement at the same time.

"Yes, I am Greek, and I am named after Alexander the Great, and I come from Macedonia as he did," he said proudly. "Do you know where that is?"

"I am sorry," said Sarah. "I know little about the world; I have been taught only about the Hebrew Scriptures and the history of my people."

"But certainly you know of Alexander the Great; he conquered the whole world."

"I know he conquered Jerusalem," said Sarah defensively. "I also know that our most hated enemy, more hated than even the Romans was another Greek: Antiochus Epiphanes! He looted our Temple; he took everything that was in it, the holy candlesticks, the altar, the curtains, everything. He would not allow the daily sacrifices and killed anyone who was a true believer. He carried away ten thousand men, women, and children to be slaves, and more than that. In our holy Temple, he set up an idol of Zeus, and offered swine — swine! — on the altar. If God had not brought deliverance through Judas Maccabees, we would have been destroyed as a nation. Every year we celebrate this victory at the Feast of Lights, and we will until the end of time!" She started to march away.

"But," said Alex, "that was more than a century ago; can't you forgive and forget?"

For a while he let her walk; then he said quietly, "And I would never do a thing like that; I believe we should be tolerant of the religion of others. I am

24

glad to see that you are a true believer in your God."

Sarah thought about that for a moment and then decided to change the subject. "My name is Sarah. Are you a slave, too?" she asked.

"Yes, I am," said Alex quickly, "and banished from my own country. You are not the only one who has troubles because of Rome."

"I am sorry to hear that," Sarah said. She realized that she had allowed self-pity to take over. Perhaps if she showed some compassion for Alex, she could take her mind off her own troubles. She had forgotten that others had problems as well, so she asked him with genuine concern, "How did this happen?"

Alex hesitated and thought for a while. How could he tell his long story in just a few words? And did she really want to know about the sad things that had happened? He decided he would make his story as brief as possible, but it would be good to talk to someone who would understand. So he began.

"My father is a philosopher and a very wise man. My nation has had some of the wisest teachers the world has ever seen." He paused; perhaps he should not have said that. He could have left off that last part: Sarah probably had never heard of Plato or Socrates or Aristotle. So, he hurried on. "My father had his own school and a large following of pupils because he was not only a teacher, but also a great orator; he could move people to action. That was the problem. He believed in liberty, justice, and democracy, and Rome did not take kindly to these ideas. Some of his students staged an insurrection, and my father was arrested and declared to be an enemy of Rome. At first, they sentenced him to death, but then they decided to be merciful, and his penalty was banishment and slavery. A wealthy landowner in Galilee was looking for a teacher to give his sons a Greek education, so he bought my father and mother and me! Bought us as a man would buy a donkey! So there is my father, a great philosopher, a wise man, teaching two boys who really don't want to learn."

For a long time, Sarah walked silently, not knowing what to say. Then she asked, "Why are you going to Jerusalem?"

"I am a craftsman and there was very little call for my skills in Galilee, so my master made arrangements with one of his friends in Jerusalem to take me. It seems that every pilgrim to Jerusalem wants souvenirs to take home — rings, seals, models of the Temple — so it is a thriving business. If I do well, I can buy my freedom in a few years."

"How can you be a craftsman?" countered Sarah. "You are too young to be a craftsman."

"It's ability that counts, not age," said Alex. "When I was just a young boy, I discovered that I had the ability to carve well. I carved every animal I could see, and even sold some of these. The idol maker saw my work and gave me a job, and soon I was as good as any in the shop.''

''Do you mean to say that you make idols? That is an abomination to God!'' said Sarah sternly. ''How could you do that?''

''People need to worship something,'' said Alex with a shrug, ''and those images are a work of art. Besides, we don't really worship the image; it is the concept of greatness behind it that matters.''

''But there is only one true God, and He made the heavens and earth,'' said Sarah with a tone of authority.

''It may be as you say,'' replied Alex thoughtfully. Then he added, ''I really don't know. Let's talk about something else. I don't want you to make a convert out of me.'' And then he smiled at her as though he were saying, ''Let's not dwell on the things that divide us; I want to be your friend.''

Later that day, Sarah went to talk with Benazra. Here was a man who certainly knew many things she would have to learn, and he seemed willing to answer her questions. They talked about many different things, but then Sarah became silent, trying to decide whether she should ask the one question that really troubled her. Finally, she blurted out, ''What is going to happen to me? What will be my fate?''

''Sarah, do not fear the future,'' Benazra said, ''because fear can rob you of your strength and courage. Many things happen to us in life which seem to threaten us, but there is a God in Heaven who hears our prayers, and He cares for us.''

''It doesn't seem as though He has heard mine,'' said Sarah with despair in her voice. ''If He had, I wouldn't be here!''

Benazra stopped, turned to her, looked into her eyes, and said, ''Are you sure, Sarah? Are you sure? You may learn later that God has been guiding you every step of the way.''

''If I could only believe that,'' Sarah said, her voice trailing away. Could she believe this? ''If that is true . . .'' she said in a whisper. She would have to think about this.

Finally the journey was almost over; they were approaching Jerusalem. Benazra called out, ''Halt! Stop right here! Sarah, come with me; I want you to see something.'' Together they walked a short way to the top of a small hill, and there was Jerusalem! Sarah drew in her breath and stood in wonder. Then Benazra quoted reverently, ''Great is the Lord, and greatly to be praised in the city of our God, in the mountain of His holiness. Beautiful for situation, the joy of the whole earth, is mount Zion, on the sides of the north, the city of the great King.''

Sarah breathed quietly, "This is the Holy City!"

Benazra knew the city well. Even though he was from Damascus, he had come to Jerusalem for the Passover every year since he was twelve, and Jerusalem had been a regular stop on his trade route. He began to point out the places of interest, the high walls dominated by many towers, the fortress of Antonia which housed the Roman garrison, the palace of King Herod, but especially, yes especially, the Temple.

Pointing to the Temple, he said with great emotion, "That is the most beautiful building in the world! The late afternoon sun makes the stone glisten like snow, and the gold flashes with beauty, even at this distance."

Benazra was not simply stating the opinion of a pious Jew; many who had seen other great buildings and temples of the world said the same thing. When Herod had begun building, that had been his aim — to build the most magnificent structure in the world. He had planned well and had poured in endless wealth. Even before he began to build, he ordered the construction of one thousand wagons to haul the great stones, most of them almost forty feet long, twelve feet wide, and eighteen feet high. He hired workmen — ten thousand of them — and since this was priestly work, he trained one thousand priests wearing priestly garments to work with stone and wood. Then came the task of building the Temple itself, and the workmen worked so diligently and so skillfully [they said that it never rained in the daytime to interrupt the work] the Temple was finished in a year and a half. During the celebration of the Dedication, Herod sacrificed three hundred oxen.

Benazra told Sarah, "One of the greatest experiences of your life will be to go to the Temple for the first time."

"Will I be allowed to go?" asked Sarah in surprise, "I will be a slave."

"Oh, yes, you will be allowed to go. No good Israelite would keep another from worshiping God," replied Benazra. "Now come. Tonight we will stay at the inn, and tomorrow, we shall go into the city."

6

Morning at Jerusalem. Sarah had not slept well; she had been thinking too much. At breakfast, she had said very little. Benazra had gone into Jerusalem already; she wondered what he was doing. Her fate hung on the decisions he was making. When breakfast was over, one of the camel drivers named Judah said, "Come with me, Alex and Sarah; we are going to meet Benazra at the slave market."

So it was finally happening! This was why Benazra had refused to answer her questions about her future. He knew but did not want to frighten her. As she walked, she quietly repeated one of the Psalms to herself to calm her spirit: " 'He that dwelleth in the secret place of the Most High shall abide under the shadow of the Almighty.' " *Oh, Lord,* she thought, *I do not know where I shall dwell, I do not know where I shall lay my head this night.* Then she went on: " 'I will say of the Lord, He is my refuge and my fortress: my God; in Him will I trust.' " She paused and breathed a prayer, *Oh, Lord, be my refuge; help me to trust.* She began to feel a calmness and a peace descending over her as she quoted the Psalm she had learned as a child in what seemed like a far-off time, in a far-off place. " 'Surely He shall deliver thee . . .' " *Oh, Lord, deliver me from the dangers I see before me.* " 'He shall cover thee with His feathers, and under his wings shalt thou trust.' " An image from her childhood flashed before her mind . . . the hen with her chicks, how she covered them, sheltered them in danger.

"Sarah, Sarah! I have been talking to you." It was Alex. "You are so quiet; what are you thinking?" He suspected that he knew.

Sarah did not want to tell him she had been praying; he would not understand. So she said only, "I have tried to find out from Benazra what is going to happen to me, but he always avoids the question. I think it is so bad he wants to hide it from me."

"Don't think that way, Sarah. I think that he avoids answering because final arrangements have not yet been made. It is Benazra's job to see that it comes out right. I trust Benazra to find me a good place." Alex's confidence encouraged Sarah and she felt a little better.

They arrived at the slave market just as activity was beginning. Sarah saw the stone upon which the slave being sold would stand so all could gawk and pass judgment. She was mortified. Could she stand this humiliation?

A narrow awning shaded half the narrow street, and the morning sun cast distinct shadows on the cobblestones. Sarah now stood with Alex under the shade of the awning. A little farther away, Judah sat on a small stool and talked to the man at the next station. He evidently knew the man and they seemed to be sharing the news. The other man was large, and although it was obvious that he was past middle age, it was also obvious that any man, slave or otherwise, would be a fool to tangle with him.

"So, what is the news?" asked Judah. "What is happening in the golden city, the center of the world?" He crossed his legs, leaned back against the pillar that supported the awning, and gave a wry smile so that one could not tell whether he believed that Jerusalem was indeed "the golden city, the center of the world," or whether, having seen the things that went on in the back streets and even here in the slave market, he was mocking this lofty reputation.

"Oh, I have news, all right! I have news!" The man pulled up a small stool that seemed all the smaller because of his bulk and settled upon it. Then he smiled and paused to let Judah wait in anticipation to make the news seem all the more dramatic. The story he had to tell, however, did not need any theatrical staging. It had captured the ears of all Jerusalem. The man relished the chance to share this gossip with someone who had not heard, to fresh ears, so he would tell the tale and savor the amazement on Judah's face.

"Have you heard what our benevolent king has done? For a long time, and without reason, he has hated two of his sons, Alexander and Aristo. He has tried to do away with them but was afraid of what Caesar would say. So, he finally lied. He told Caesar he had proof that they were going to kill him, so Caesar said he could put them on trial. Some trial! Herod would not even let his sons out of prison to speak for themselves, nor would he let anyone say a word for them. Everyone in Jerusalem knew they were good sons, but no one dared to say a word because all feared the wrath of the king. We were even afraid to speak about it because word might be carried to Herod by his spies, and it would be the end of us, too. It was mighty tense in Jerusalem, I'll tell you."

"What happened to the sons?" asked Judah.

"I'm getting to that; just wait. I said that everyone was afraid to speak. Well, there was one old man named Tero who went to Herod and told him to his face that he was wrong and should let his sons go. We all breathed a sigh of relief and hoped that the madness had been averted. The next thing we heard, Herod's sniveling barber mentioned that this Tero had said that he should cut Herod's throat during the next shave. He would be a hero and three hundred of Herod's own officers would regard him. That did it! The king arrested Tero, his sons, the three hundred officers, and, listen to this, the barber! Herod had all of them stoned to death, and then he had his sons, his own sons, strangled in prison. Now what do you think about a king like that?''

Sarah listened to this and could not believe her ears. What kind of father would do this to his sons? What kind of man could be so filled with violence? What kind of man could be so cruel? *Oh, God in Heaven, please muzzle this monster who is called our king.*

Sarah had been so intent listening to this story that she had not noticed two men who stood across the street looking at her, watching her. She did notice them, however, when one man began pointing to her and then engaged the other in earnest conversation. What were they talking about? What were they saying about her? Oh, no, that couldn't be. But here they were in the slave market. What if they were looking for a slave to buy? What if that was what the conversation was all about? They crossed the street and stood in front of her.

"Look at her, Nabus." It was the older of the two that was speaking. He was wearing a dirty robe, his hair was unkempt, and his hands were in need of washing. His appearance repulsed Sarah.

"She is only a child, Abul — only a child." It was the second man speaking, and he was about to turn and walk away. Abul grabbed him by the shoulder and turned him around.

"Only a child? Have you no eyes? Can you not see what is before you? You say that she is a child, but if you will just imagine what is under that cheap cloak, you will find, not a child, as you think, but a woman."

Sarah could not look at those men; she had never felt such shame! She could not move. She tried to shut out the whole scene, the men, the conversation she had heard, the slave market, all of it! She tried to imagine that she was back in her little town working in the barley field, singing and praying, back to the tranquility and peace, to the safety and security she had known only a few days ago. Surely this was nothing but a bad dream, and she would wake up soon. She shut her eyes tightly, trying to make reality disappear, but it did no good. She could not escape.

Abul walked behind her. She could smell some kind of food on his dirty garment. She could almost feel his presence, and she shivered with disgust and fear. And then she felt his hands on her body. She was too terrified to scream or move. She stood like stone.

"Nabus, we could afford to offer a good price for this one. Look at that beautiful face, those dark eyes; never mind that they are red; she has probably been crying; but she will get used to it. We could make money on her."

"Perhaps you are right, Abul. Some rich merchant would probably like a girl like that for a concubine."

"Are you a fool, Nabus? I don't intend to sell her once and make one profit. I have better plans than that for her!"

No one had to explain to Sarah what the man's plans were. She knew. If it came to this, she would die!

"I say yes," said the other man. "Let's take her."

Judah was listening to all of this but said nothing. Then Abul came over to him and said, "You are indeed fortunate today. We are willing to pay a fair price for the girl. What is she worth?"

Judah looked at the dirty man standing before him, and he disliked him immediately. He did not care to enter into discussion with him, so he simply said, "I am not in charge here. You will have to talk to the trader when he returns."

"And when will he return?"

"He will be back in an hour."

"Then tell him that you have a buyer for the girl, a buyer who is willing to pay good money. We will be back in an hour, but do not sell her before that." Then they walked down the street to find something to eat.

Sarah turned to Alex in panic. "Alex, can you help me? You saved me once; will you do it again? Please!"

"I am sorry, Sarah. You know I would if I could. If I thought it would do any good, I would fight the man with my bare hands, most gladly would I fight him! But it would do no good. You would suffer, and I would suffer. There is nothing I can do." But then he thought for a moment, and added, "You must pray to your God."

"Will you pray, too?" pleaded Sarah, looking for all the help she could find.

"Me pray? To my gods? That would do no good. My gods do not know what is happening to us; and, if they did, they would not care. They are so cruel and deceitful to each other, that I would not trust them to care for my affairs. Besides, Fate arranges these things, and there is nothing we can do about it. Things happen as they happen, sometimes good, sometimes bad, and it doesn't matter if we are good or bad; it happens to all of us alike."

"Do not say that, Alex. There is a God in Heaven who knows and who cares!"

"Oh, I would like to believe that! I would truly like to see your God deliver you from that beast that wants to buy you and abuse you; and, if I thought that my prayer to your God would do any good, I would pray, too."

Sarah stood silently and prayed. Alex, despite his heart of unbelief, prayed, too.

In due time, Benazra returned, and Judah began to tell him of the offer he had received for Sarah. Benazra almost laughed and said to him, "Do you think I would let her go to a man like that? He couldn't find enough money in the world to buy her!"

Sarah was elated. She looked at Alex as though to say, "See, there is a God in Heaven. He heard and answered prayer." But her elation did not last long, because she heard Benazra saying, "Come with me, Sarah, you are going to be working in the palace of King Herod."

Sarah was stunned; thoughts raced through her mind. How could she go to the palace of this vile king? She was not prepared for this, but since the last episode had frightened her so much, the other possibilities were so devastating, this announcement was almost a relief. Surely Benazra would not allow her to be placed in a situation that would destroy her, would he?

"What will I have to do there?" she asked.

"I do not know," replied Benazra, "but you will find out soon enough. Often we cannot choose our surroundings, but at least we can make the best of them. You have the idea that you might be like an Esther," he teased good-naturedly. "If that is to be true, you couldn't find a better place than the king's palace."

That did not encourage Sarah; it frightened her. This was more than she had bargained for. Back in Ebba she had dreamed of what she would do as a deliverer; now she wished that she could find some obscure place and do some humble task.

"You have no choice, Sarah," said Benazra. "Most of these arrangements were made before we left, but I was not sure until this morning. I am sorry that I was not able to tell you anything in case things did not work out, but how would you have felt if I had told you that first day that you were going to Herod's palace? This way is best. You are strong, and you trust in God; I know you will be all right."

"And what about Alex?" asked Sarah.

"After I take you to the palace, I will see about his arrangements; but don't worry. I will do a good job for him, the best job I can do. He will be in Jerusalem, too, and I am quite sure you will see each other again."

Alex was relieved for Sarah's sake but also sad to see Sarah go. He did not know how to say good-bye, but he said awkwardly, "Sarah, I have known you for only a few days, but I have learned much from you, and I hope that the God you serve will protect you."

For her part, Sarah was even less prepared with a farewell speech, but she said, "Thank you for all you have done. I hope we meet again." As they turned to leave, once again Sarah thought, *How inadequate that was. There is so much more that I should have said.*

Sarah and Benazra arrived at the palace, which was really more of a city than a house. They went around to a side gate which was protected by one of Herod's guards. *He is tall,* Sarah thought — the tallest man she had ever seen — with blond hair and blue eyes.

How imposing and powerful he looked in his battle dress! Sarah later learned that Herod had a personal bodyguard of four hundred men: Germans, Thracians, and Gauls. In addition to this, when Cleopatra died, her personal guard was given to Herod by Caesar. This was like a fortified city.

The guard opened the gate, and they went to the back door where they were met by a matronly looking woman named Leah. "Here's your girl," said Benazra. "She is a good girl, and you will find that she is dependable. Please treat her well."

"I will treat her well," Leah assured him.

"I am so glad to hear that," replied Benazra. "I have taken a liking to this girl; she deserves better than life has given her so far." Then he turned to Sarah and said, "I pray that the God of Heaven will bless you and keep you, and make His face to shine upon you, and give you peace."

His voice was filled with emotion, and when Sarah opened her mouth to speak, no words would come out. She stood and watched him go.

Sarah stood with Leah in the kitchen of the palace and looked around. How large, how rich everything seemed. Her whole house would fit into one corner of this room. Leah smiled at Sarah's reaction; she knew it would be impossible for a young girl from Galilee to imagine such wealth. Then she said, "This is grander than your previous home, isn't it? But this is only the kitchen. Let me show you the rest of the palace; you will need to know your way around."

When Herod built his palace, he spared no expense. He imported the richest materials from all over the world. It had marble halls, heated pools, rich hangings and tapestries covering the walls. In Galilee they had to be content with a charcoal fire in the center of the room when the nights were cold; the palace was heated with a furnace that brought warm air through all the walls and floors. Gold and silver and precious stones were found everywhere.

On the way back to the kitchen, Leah said, "You have no idea how the wealthy live; but you will soon find out. Now, sit down; let's talk about you and what is expected of you here."

"Am I a slave here?" Sarah asked.

"Let's not think of you as a slave; let's just call you a servant. After all, this is Jerusalem and not Rome. The Scriptures command us to treat slaves with kindness. However, you are expected to do what you are told and to be faithful in your tasks. If you are, you will not have a hard time with me," she said forthrightly.

"What do you expect me to do?" asked Sarah with some apprehension.

"Herod is old and sick, and we need more help with him. He does not sleep well at night and is always demanding something. His chamberlain needs a dependable girl to get what he asks for and often to summon the physician."

"I have heard much about the king, and I am afraid of him," said Sarah.

"My dear girl," said Leah, "you must remember that we did not bring you here to vote on your job, or to decide what you will do or won't do. You have no choice. The king is suspicious of everyone, so the chamberlain, Joseph, thought that a girl would be the best choice to serve this way. You must be wise enough to avoid the king's anger, but Joseph does not believe that you will be in any real danger. The king wants someone to show him kindness without expecting anything in return. He has often complained that everyone around him wants something from him, and perhaps he is right. He is surrounded by people who grovel and flatter him. The king knows that, and I think he hates them all. He does not trust the slaves in the palace; he thinks they are all plotting against him. You do not know any of them, and it would be best if you kept it that way so that you will avoid suspicion. Now, come with me; I want you to meet Joseph. You are to do whatever he tells you, but you will answer to me."

Joseph was the king's chamberlain, but he was much more than a butler. Since he was so close to the king, he knew what was going on, he knew how the king felt about matters, and the king trusted him as an advisor.

Sarah liked Joseph immediately. He seemed like a wise, dignified man. His hair was beginning to gray, and he was bald on top; his beard was full and dark. After a brief conversation with Sarah, he said to Leah, "I am pleased with her. You have made a good choice; and, I am sure that the king will be pleased as well. Her room will be the little one next to mine so I can summon her easily during the night." He turned to the girl. "Let me give you a little advice, Sarah; when dealing with the king, speak little, listen much, and you will be fine."

Sarah was shown her room. It was small; it was a slave's room. But the floor was marble and the furniture was more elegant than she had ever seen. Left alone in her room, she poured out thanksgiving to God, who had delivered her at the inn yard and when she had prayed in the slave market, and had brought her safely here. Then she prayed for her dear father. She wondered where he was; she knew that he must still be brokenhearted at their parting and filled with anxiety for her safety. Oh, how she wished she could let him know that God had been faithful to her.

"And, dear Lord," she pleaded, "continue to guide me. I feel like a stranger in a foreign land."

As the Sabbath approached, Sarah noticed a change in the pace of activities in the palace. Preparations had to be made for the coming day, because, even for the slaves of the palace, the Sabbath was a day of rest. While Sarah was with Leah in the kitchen, Leah said to her, "The Sabbath begins in just a few hours. Help me finish with this. Then I will show you your way to the Temple. Remember this," she advised, "in spite of any other circumstances in your life, your true home is the house of God. Center your thoughts on that, not on the things that are not as they should be."

When the time came, Leah and Sarah went up to the Temple. As they were going, Leah recited, " 'I was glad when they said unto me, Let us go into the house of the Lord, Our feet shall stand within thy gates, O Jerusalem. Peace be within thy walls, and prosperity within thy palaces.' "

As they approached the Temple, Sarah decided that she could endure the struggles and degradation of being a slave in Herod's palace if she could worship every Sabbath in this place, the dwelling place of the Almighty God.

The Temple did not disappoint her. It was situated high above the surrounding city. As they ascended a flight of steps, they came to a massive gate. Every other gate into the Temple was of gold; this one was of polished Corinthian brass, but it was no less magnificent than the others. Indeed, this is the gate that had the name, the Beautiful Gate. Passing through this, they came into the Court of the Women.

Once inside the grounds, Sarah stood and stared at the Temple. "It's so beautiful!" she whispered. "I didn't know anything could be so wonderful."

The Temple building was surrounded by porches, the roofs of which were supported by high, carved columns. The double doors to the Temple were as high as the building itself, and they were covered from top to bottom with gold plates. Above the gates was a large golden vine with grapes.

She was delighted to be a part of the worshiping throng; she felt that she had come to her spiritual home. She was delighted with what she saw; but she was also disappointed with some things that she had not expected to see. In the Court of the Gentiles sat the money changers, loudly doing business. How out of place that seemed! Leah noticed that she was looking at them with obvious displeasure, and said, "Those men are nothing but thieves, but we have no choice. They are the only source of Temple coins; we are at their mercy. And look at that!"

Sarah turned and was surprised to see a large market with men selling animals for the sacrifices. It was a noisy, oversized butcher shop! Sarah said to Leah, "How can that be? Here in such beautiful, sacred surroundings?"

One more thing struck a discordant note for her: the beggars! There were so many of them; and many had made their conditions appear far worse than they really were to evoke pity, and, consequently, a greater share of the alms from generous worshipers. All of the confusion detracted from the atmosphere of worship.

But the evening sacrifice was about to begin, so Sarah turned her thoughts to spiritual things. She said to herself, " 'Serve the Lord with gladness; come before His presence with singing. Enter into His gates with thanksgiving, and into His courts with praise: be thankful unto Him, and bless His name. For the Lord is good; His mercy is everlasting; and His truth endureth to all generations.' "

She bowed her head, and worshiped.

7

Life in Jerusalem was far different from life in Galilee, and life in the palace was far different from life in ordinary homes. Sarah could see the enormous wealth of the palace, but nothing prepared her for the extravagant display she saw at a banquet held only a few days after her arrival. Banquets were a favorite form of entertainment for the rich and powerful. Each tried to outdo the others, and Herod was in a position to outdo them all. He intended to do so.

The guests began arriving in the afternoon, many of them in ornate conveyances with long poles carried by a slave at each corner. When the first one arrived, Sarah watched a woman emerge. She could not believe her eyes. The woman was clothed in an elegant silk gown held together with clasps of gold covered with jewels. Her fingers were covered with rings. She wore heavy makeup on her face, and to Sarah it seemed much overdone. No foreign substance had ever touched her face! But it was the woman's hair that amazed Sarah the most. It had been dyed blonde and piled on top of her head in a most elaborate fashion. For her headdress she wore, as a crown, a representation of the city of Jerusalem! It had cost a small fortune.

The others who arrived presented the same gaudiness. Here was a show of the finest silk and linen garments to be found anywhere. Gold, silver, and jewels added to the lavish display.

Invitations carefully drawn by artists had been sent out two days before the king's feast; and, just before the feast, servants were sent to each person with the message, "All things are ready; come to the feast." They began arriving early in the afternoon, and the feast would go on well into the night.

When the guests arrived, a servant would wash their hands and feet and bring them to their assigned places. Some of the women wore sandals so special that they were entrusted only to their own servants who had been brought along. The guests reclined on couches surrounding low tables. The banquet hall had been decorated to look like a garden, with plants and flowers and living trees. The musicians were playing, and a small army of servants in the kitchen made final preparations.

Each guest was given a menu so that he could plan his choices as the feast proceeded but also to impress the guests with the variety and richness of the food. Each course was served separately. Since they ate with their fingers, following each course, a servant would bring each person a bowl of water and a towel. It was Sarah's task to bring the bowl and towel to the king.

The feast began. The servants entered the hall with large silver and bronze trays laden with danties, shellfish, salted fish from Galilee served on slices of cucumber, and eggs with onions. The next course was soup, brought to each table in a large steaming pot, and served in ornate bowls with matching spoons. This was followed by wine with honey, served in glass goblets.

The courses followed one after another — omelets, boiled meat, pigeons, quails, pancakes, and finally dessert of pastry, fruits, and wines. To a girl who had grown up in simple surroundings where food was simple and scarce, this was overwhelming! She was amazed at the variety and quantity of the food, but since she had known the poverty of most of the people, this seemed a wasteful display.

But the evening was more than food. When the dishes had been cleared away, the musicians struck up a lively tune. The guests entered in and began clapping their hands in time with the music, and the dancing girls appeared. This part of the program was followed by comedians, acrobats, and jugglers, followed by more dancing girls, followed by more wine. Then came speeches, and finally the evening was over.

Except for the cleanup, which took most of the night!

As time passed, Sarah performed well and earned Leah's trust. She was given additional responsibilities and, to her delight, additional mobility.

One day, Sarah was leaving the palace by the back gate to go on an errand. The gate guard knew her and spoke to her as he opened the gate. It was a good day, and Sarah had a song in her heart.

As she turned the corner, she noticed a group of young men watching her. She was not frightened by this; after all, this was Jerusalem, and Roman soldiers would arrive quickly at any sign of commotion. So she did not hurry away as the young man, who appeared to be the leader, came toward her. In fact, Sarah thought, *Now there is a handsome young man! Why should he want to speak to me?*

The young man approached her and said, "We have been watching you for some time. Are you a true daughter of Israel? Do you weep at the oppression we suffer under the heel of Rome?"

"I am a true daughter of Israel," replied Sarah and added uncautiously, "and sometimes I would like God to make me like Queen Esther to bring deliverance."

The young man warned, "Speak softly; we must not be overheard. My name is Joash; what is yours?"

Sarah laughed, and whispered, "I was going to say Esther, but you can call me Sarah."

"And you work in Herod's palace?"

"Yes, I am a maid, and I help to serve the king."

Joash replied, "Perhaps God has brought us together at just the right time. We are students of the Pharisee teacher, Mattias, and we are all willing to lay down our lives for Israel. Three of our number have done that recently."

"Laid down their lives?" asked Sarah naively. "How did they do that?" She was just beginning to sense the danger of Esther's job.

"They were apprehended by Herod's guards in our secret meeting place. It was only by God's grace that we were not all captured. A spy must have told them our location. Without a trial, Herod condemned them to death, and they were thrown to the lions in the arena. We do not attend those heathen games at the arena, but that time we had to go to pray as they met their deaths with courage. They were led into the arena, empty-handed, and six starving lions were turned loose on them. The lions tore them apart and sat down to devour them. The crowd cheered."

Joash was overcome with emotion, as though he was reliving the terrible event. After a while he continued, "Right then, five of our members took an oath to kill Herod, even though it will cost them their lives, too. Herod is always surrounded by his bodyguards; but, the next time he attends the theater, these five will be hiding where they can strike him before the guards are aware of what is happening. There will be no escape for them; they will be true martyrs. But we need someone inside the palace to find out when he will be attending the theater. Can you do this?"

Sarah did not hesitate. "I can do that!"

"It may be dangerous," said Joash.

"I can do it!" replied Sarah.

Joash was pleased. "Then meet us next Sabbath in the Court of the Women just before the evening sacrifice, and we will do the rest; and may the God of Israel protect us all."

It was not difficult for Sarah to obtain the information; it was no secret in the palace that Herod was going to the theater on Tuesday night. Sarah could hardly wait for the Sabbath. What she was doing was dangerous, but that made it exciting. Beside that, although she did not want to admit it, even to herself, she had a warm feeling, a strange feeling inside of her whenever she thought of Joash.

At the Temple, she saw Joash standing near one of the pillars. She went to him and simply said, "Tuesday night." He nodded and said, "You have done a good job." Then he turned and left. Sarah hoped she had not been seen.

The next day, Herod was having another banquet. He had been so sick all day that people in the palace wondered if he would be able to attend, but he told them dramatically, "It is the only pleasure I have left in life; I will go even if I must be carried in on my couch." So the banquet was held.

As the evening wore on, Herod seemed to revive. Perhaps it was the wine that dulled his pain, but he became more talkative and began to expound on his exploits and especially the times that he had wielded his power when he was challenged. Sarah had just brought in a plate of fruit when she heard him gloat, "They mocked me, those Magi! They came here looking for a newborn king of the Jews. Imagine! Newborn! As though I should have a son in my condition! Besides, I have enough sons already, although I do not trust a single one of them. So I called in the priests, and they told us about the Bethlehem prophecy. I have so many threats against my life and my position! I do not need another from Bethlehem."

Herod sank back on his couch as though he could not continue, but he cleared his throat and changed his tone, "I told them, 'I am as interested in this king as you are; I, too, would like to worship him. Find him and bring me word.' I should have sent my bodyguard with them. They never returned; they mocked me! But I solved the problem. I sent Horo and his men to Bethlehem, and they did a good job." He laughed viciously. "Every boy two years old and younger — put to the sword! You never heard such weeping and lamenting!"

Sarah had to leave the room quickly. King of the Jews — What did this mean? And was the king destroyed? Then she said to herself, "Herod, you are nothing but a monster! I weep for all those mothers whose babies were snatched from them and killed before their eyes. I will avenge them! Villain, you shall not live! I will poison the wine you drink tonight!"

Leah noticed that Sarah was agitated and speaking to herself, so she came over and asked, "Sarah, what is the matter? What has happened to make you so upset?"

Sarah struggled to regain her composure, but she said, "Herod was just bragging how he ordered the babies of Bethlehem killed; he was rejoicing in that! I will avenge them! Herod has a golden box on his table, and I know what is in it; it is poison from Egypt. Tonight I will put some in his wine, and he will go to face the God who judges such things."

Aware of the others who might overhear their conversation, Leah said, "Sarah! do not talk that way. Keep your voice down, or it will be bad for you. And do not be rash. He cannot live much longer. Leave the judgment to God."

Sarah's anger began to subside, especially when she considered that in two days it would be Tuesday, and Herod would meet his fate at the hands of those who were sure to do the job in the theater.

8

It was Tuesday afternoon, and Sarah was busy working in the courtyard when she heard a commotion at the gate. One of the guards was calling to another, "Come here and help me; this fellow who calls himself Sostee claims he has information about a plot against the king's life at the theater tonight. Take him to Herod, and let him tell his story."

Sarah froze in her tracks. The gate swung open and in came the man they called Sostee. Sarah recognized him; he was one of the men in the group with Joash. Their eyes met. Surely he recognized her! One mention of her name to Herod would mean her death. She went through the motions of her task, her mind racing. Somehow she would have to warn Joash. She decided to wait until Sostee left to see if his warning had been taken seriously. Perhaps that would decide everything. If he mentioned her, she would have no more decisions to make — ever.

It seemed like an eternity, but finally he left. Sarah made sure that he did not see her again. She waited for someone to come and apprehend her, but no one came. She decided that she had to take the chance to warn the others. She approached the gate guard and tried to appear casual, commenting about the weather; but when she told him she had to go out on an errand, he said, "No one is allowed to leave for any reason. There has been a plot against the king's life, and we will catch them red-handed. I would not like to be in their shoes!"

When it came time to go to the theater, the gate opened, but Herod did not appear. Instead, a company of bodyguards in full battle dress marched out toward the theater. Sarah watched them go, but she was helpless. They had received accurate information; they knew where the men were hiding. The next day, Herod passed sentence upon each of them. They were taken outside the city and beaten to death. Sarah waited for her own punishment, but nothing happened. Somehow she had escaped the danger.

The next Sabbath, Sarah sought out Joash and told him, "Sostee is the traitor."

"How do you know that?" asked Joash skeptically. "He seems to be a true believer and a faithful student."

Sarah told Joash what she had seen and heard. Joash nodded sadly. "It all makes sense," he said. "We have known that there must have been a traitor on the inside to know our plans, not only this time, but several times before. Herod's guards knew just where to look for the men, resistance was useless, and now they are all dead. May God judge Sostee for his deeds!"

"What are you going to do about it?" asked Sarah.

"First of all, we are going to make sure that he is not in on any future plans; then we will see."

Three days later, there was a riot in the streets of Jerusalem, and Sostee was beaten to death by an angry mob. When Sarah heard it, she was dismayed and horrified. She did not know how she should feel. Sostee had caused the death of the men who trusted him as a friend. He deserved it! But on the other hand he could have accused Sarah as part of the conspiracy, and he didn't; he spared her life. Her spirit was in turmoil.

The next night Herod was in great pain. Again and again the physicians had ordered medicated wine, but nothing seemed to help. Sarah had just brought another cup, put it on the table beside his bed, and was leaving when he called out, "Stop, girl, I want to talk to you."

Sarah was startled; she dreaded what would follow. Why should he want to talk to her?

Then Herod said, "Do you know what it is like to feel guilty? Do you know what it is like to have caused the death of someone?"

Sarah was terrified. He knew! This was the end for her. She turned to look at Herod, expecting to see his face contorted with rage. She was surprised to see that he was not even looking at her.

"Sit down," he commanded. Sarah sat trembling on the floor, her hands folded in her lap, her eyes downcast, waiting for what would follow.

"I am guilty," said Herod. Then he drew in his breath and shouted, "I am guilty! Do you know how that feels?"

Sarah started to nod, but then she saw that he was not waiting for an answer. He had been drinking so much medicated wine that he was hardly aware of her presence.

"I am suffering the judgment of God," he continued. "I have killed the only person I ever loved. Oh, yes, they will tell you that I have had ten wives, but I have really only had one, and I killed her. Oh, Marian, what have I done to you?"

He looked around the room, searching the dark corners, as though he expected to see her there. Then he said, almost in a whisper, "Where are you, Marian? Come to me. Come lie beside me. I need you!"

Sarah was frightened by his talk, but she could only sit there and listen.

"I saw her first in Samaria," said the king. He smiled as though he were seeing her again, as he did the first time. "She was the most beautiful woman in the world. She was a Maccabean princess. I was overcome by her beauty. I had to have her. And I did!" he added with emphasis. Then he was silent as though he were reliving his life with his queen. Then he said angrily, "No, I never had her; I never really had her. I was never sure of her, but I could not bear the thought of someone else having her. Yes, I was jealous! Jealousy ate at me, destroying me."

Then he was silent, and Sarah thought he was through; but he began again, "When I had to go to Rome and leave her behind, I gave orders to a trusted friend that, if I did not return, she should be killed so she could not belong to another man. And my trusted friend told her! I killed him for that. Marian never forgave me for it. She threatened to leave me. I couldn't let her go."

Then Herod began to weep as only a drunken man can weep. After he recovered, he repeated reasonably, "She knew I couldn't let her go; so she taunted me, teased me, ignored me, refused me. Me! the great king! I was her captive."

He tried to sit up in bed to give some display of regal dignity, but he could not. Sarah thought, *How sad; how pathetic.*

"They brought accusations against her," he said in a whisper, "accusations that she was unfaithful to me; accusations that she was plotting against me. They were not true, but jealousy consumed me. I gave her a trial — Ha! what a mockery! I had decided her fate before the first word was spoken. And I killed her! I killed her!"

Then the sobbing began as though the floodgates had burst open. He was shaking and coughing, tears coursing down his cheeks. Sarah was afraid to move. When Herod sobered up, would he pursue the one who had heard his private confessions? Would he hunt and kill her, too?

In the midst of the weeping, he cried out, "But there is more, there is more. I also killed her two sons — my two sons — and I killed her mother, and I killed the whole Maccabean family; none is left." He let out a loud wail, and the sobbing began again. Finally, the sobbing melted into moans, and it appeared that he was drifting into a stupor. Lying there with his eyes closed, he murmured, "Now the judgment of God is upon me for my evil deeds. My body itches so, I can hardly stand it; I am covered with open sores. Inside I am being eaten by worms and nothing can kill them; and the pain in my head! I am damned!"

He let out a loud wail, and then was silent. His breathing was labored, and the heavy medication was taking effect. Sarah stood at the door and looked back into the room. In the flickering light of the oil lamps, things had an unreal appearance. The king, an old man, now seventy years of age, looked small and wizened in the oversized gold bed. The richly embroidered bed covers mocked the degenerate condition of his body, afflicted with so many ills. How he could keep on living was a mystery.

Perhaps he will be gone in the morning, Sarah thought; *then Israel can have peace.*

But he would not be gone by morning. This man who seemed so weak and powerless was still capable of immense damage and treachery, as Sarah would learn. He was not through yet!

The Sabbath after the death of Sostee, Sarah sought out Joash in the Temple porch. "I need your help," she told him. "I feel so guilty about what I did. Did I do the right thing to tell you that Sostee was the spy?"

"Of course you did," replied Joash. "We had trusted him, and he would have destroyed all of us if he had not been uncovered."

"But a human life is precious, even the life of a traitor," said Sarah, unconvinced.

"Indeed, human life is precious," agreed Joash; "but now, because of that madman and his hirelings, it is wasted like water poured out in the dirt, not only here in Jerusalem but also in all our land. Nobody is safe. I fear for you in Herod's palace, especially. If the king becomes suspicious or displeased with you for any reason, he will not hesitate to have you killed."

Then he added, "I should be very sad if anything happened to you."

Sarah blushed at these words. No one had ever spoken to her like that. She had to admit she had feelings for Joash that she could not understand. She had been telling herself that she admired him simply because of his devotion to liberty, but it was more than that. Sadly, she also knew that there could be no future to any relationship since she was a slave. Only a few words could pass between them there on the porch on the Sabbath, but anything more than that was out of the question. Still, she left the Temple that day, not feeling sad and guilty as she had when she came, but with a strange lightness and a joy that sent her on her way singing.

A few Sabbaths later, it was Joash who sought out Sarah. After casual greetings, he brought Sarah to the edge of the crowd and lowered his voice so they could not be overheard. Then he continued confidentially, "Our teacher, Mattias, thinks our history is about to come to a climax. God is going to do something for us. We must seize the initiative before Herod is gone and yet while he is too weak to resist us. Right now in Jerusalem there is support for a popular uprising."

He explained, "Over the Temple, the holy Temple of God, Herod installed the Roman eagle. He claims that this is just to honor Caesar, who had been his benefactor, but our teacher says it is more than that. He says that it is a Roman deity which the Roman soldiers carry into battle with them; and, before the battle, they all bow down and worship it. Because of that, no Israelite can be a Roman soldier: We will not bow down to any idol. But this idol is on our Temple.''

"I have seen that eagle on the Temple," Sarah said, "but I did not know what it was. What can we do about it?''

"Our teacher says that God will never bless us or deliver us as long as that abomination is on our holy place. Our prayers are hindered by that idol. Herod will not listen to our entreaties, so we will have to take other measures. We will have to pick a time when Herod is so ill that he will not be concerned about it. Then we will do it.''

"Do what?" Sarah asked.

"You will see at the right time," he answered mysteriously.

Sarah said, "Who will do it? I hope you won't. I would not like to see anything terrible happen to you.''

"I appreciate that, Sarah, but the person who loves his life more than his duty to God is not worthy of God. I will not only help in the task, I will be the leader," he said proudly. "You can help me though by letting me know when Herod is too weak to hinder us.''

There was no doubt that Herod's health was failing. One night he was so ill that his physician did not think he could live until morning. Before dawn, Sarah slipped out of the palace and went to the home of the disciples of Mattias. She knocked on the door quietly so the neighborhood would not be aroused. It was Joash who came to the door. He was surprised to see Sarah.

"You should not have taken the risk to come here; you must be more careful. But I think I know your message. Herod is ill, isn't he?''

"Yes. He is so ill his physician thinks he may not live out the day," said Sarah.

"Then this is the day the Lord has appointed," Joash rejoiced. "This is the day!''

Joash and his friends waited until the Temple court was full of people; what they had to do needed to be done in the sight of all — not under the cover of darkness. Into the Temple grounds they marched, carrying axes. This was enough to attract attention; so, when Joash raised his hands and called to the people, the crowd gathered to listen.

"Hear me, Oh, Israel! Listen all you people of the living God!" shouted

Joash with loud voice and great intensity. "Our God is a jealous God and will not share His glory with any other god. All the gods of the nations are idols, and an abomination to the living God who made the heavens and the earth. If we will be holy and true to Him, He will deliver us as He has in the days of our fathers. Put away evil out of your hearts, and worship Him only."

The people not only listened, but wholeheartedly supported the things spoken by Joash. It was as though he was calling for revival as did the ancient prophets, and the people were willing to respond. He continued.

"God hears the prayers of His dedicated people when their hearts are pure. But our prayers are hindered, and we are oppressed. Why? Because here above the holy dwelling place of God, we have tolerated a heathen idol — the eagle of Rome — hindering our prayers, polluting our worship, and hiding God's face from us." Then he picked up his ax, held it high, and said, "This day in the sight of all the people, we are going to destroy the idol and open the windows of Heaven so God's mercy can rain upon us."

He raised a ladder against the Temple and quickly mounted it. He climbed up to the eagle and attacked it. After a struggle, it finally came loose, and he knocked it to the ground. Then the others chopped it into small pieces with their axes. The people shouted and cheered.

When the Temple guards heard, they came on the run, expecting to find a riot in progress. They thrust their way into the midst of the crowd, anticipating violence. Instead, they saw the shattered eagle on the ground with Joash and the others standing around it. He made no effort to flee but stood waiting to be apprehended. As the guards subdued the crowd, the commander of the guards went to the palace to report to Herod.

9

When the commander arrived at the palace, Herod's physician would not let him in to see the king. "No one is allowed in," he said. "The king may be breathing his last breath. I cannot let you bother him with this."

But the commander insisted. "If he revives, as he has many times, he will go hard on us for keeping this from him. He will surely think it is a conspiracy and that we are part of it. Nothing may come of it; but, if I report it to him, we will be blameless and our lives will be spared."

The physician agreed. "You may go in for one minute — no more."

The commander entered the king's chamber with the physician. Herod weakly opened his eyes and roused a little when he saw the commander. In a weak voice he asked, "Trouble?"

The commander replied, "They have destroyed the Roman eagle that was on the Temple."

"Seize them!" Herod said and closed his eyes again.

Without another word, the commander left the room and rushed back to the Temple. With a large group of soldiers, he roughly moved through the crowd, pushing down many of the people who had been rejoicing just a short time before. Then, seizing Joash and his companions, he led them off to prison.

Two days later, Sarah was at work in the palace when she heard a great commotion. A troop of Temple guards marched through the main gate into the palace. Then her heart sank. In the midst of the soldiers, she saw Joash and his companions, their arms bound behind them.

"They are coming here for trial!" she groaned to herself, knowing all about Herod's trials.

Indeed, they were. Although Herod was so weak that he could not lift up his head, he had demanded that they be brought to trial before him. He had also summoned some of the priests and Sadducees to witness the trial. Herod would be the accuser, the judge, and the jury. Herod began to speak.

"All of you know that, at great personal expense and effort, I built the magnificent Temple which is the wonder of the whole earth." This was the

beginning of a long, arrogant oration about his good deeds and great ac-
complishments. He went on for a long while. When he finally wound down,
he said abruptly, "I accuse these traitors of conspiracy against the state, of
desecrating the Temple, and of personally insulting me, the king. They are
guilty."

Then he turned to the leaders and asked, "What do you say?" The rulers
were afraid to answer. They knew the fury of the king when he was well;
now he appeared to be out of his mind. No one dared to speak a word in
defense of the men. After a short pause, since he heard no contradiction, he
raised his hand as a regal gesture and said, "I condemn them all to be
burned at the stake!"

The word had spread rapidly through the palace. Most had been in favor
of the patriotic action and were dismayed at the harsh penalty decreed by
Herod. Was there no help?

That night Sarah cried and prayed on her bed. Had she been guilty for
this tragedy even though she had been attempting to help?

The next day, the sentence was carried out.

Joash was gone! Sarah could not believe it. It tore her heart out. She felt
that her world had come to an end. It was not only his dedication to the
cause that had attracted her so. She did not hope for a life of her own, but
she did dream of things that might have been. She could not help it; she
liked and admired Joash. She had pictured herself with him in some little
town, not Ebba, but some little town where they could live in peace and
worship God and forget about the Romans. She knew this was unrealistic,
but it was a happy dream that brought contentment with it in spite of everything. Now it was over. Joash was dead! The dream was dead!

Then she began to grow angry. Tero and the barber were dead, three hundred soldiers had been stoned, three fed to lions, five beaten to death.
Herod had even butchered his own family! Now Joash was dead, too. This
struggle against Herod and against Rome was devouring them, and they
were no closer to freedom after all of the great sacrifices. Would it devour
her, too? Was it a hopeless cause? Should she give it up? There were some
choices she had to make. But she had no choice about the storm that was
about to engulf her.

"Help! Help! The king has been poisoned!" It was the middle of the night,
and the guard's voice rang through the empty halls of the palace. Sarah rushed
from her room and ran to summon the king's physician. He ran to the king's
chamber, ordered everyone out, and shut the door. In a short time he came
out and said, "The poison was in his wine; I will do what I can to save him."

In time the commotion subsided, but the guards did not rest. Someone would have to pay for this lapse of security; someone would suffer for this. Several of the guards were in the slaves' quarters, asking questions. It seemed like a hopeless task. Then one slave came forward and volunteered some information. "It was that girl Sarah. She told Leah that she was going to do it! I heard it all."

When Leah was called, she did her best to defend Sarah; but she could not deny the conversation. "She was simply angry when she said that," was her only answer.

"And what was she angry about?" demanded the guard.

What could Leah say? The simple conversation would condemn Sarah. It all came out.

There was no knock on Sarah's door. The guards burst in and seized her.

"What are you doing to me?" she cried out.

"You are accused of poisoning the king."

"Me? I never did such a thing!"

When they told her they knew of her conversation with Leah, she knew she was trapped; it would do no good to protest further. "What are you going to do with me?" she asked in a trembling voice.

"We are taking you to the dungeon. Tomorrow the king's torturer will get the truth from you."

Sarah knew the king's torturer. She had often seen him eating with the slaves, but always by himself. He had no friends. And he was kept busy. Instead of a lawyer to ask questions, Herod used the more effective torturer; and, after awhile, even the strongest told everything they knew and even confessed to crimes that they had not committed.

Once, after a riot in the streets, Herod had his guards seize two women who merely happened to be looking out of their windows at the time. During torture, they gave the names of those who had started the riot, even though they were friends and neighbors.

This is what Sarah faced. She had done nothing; she knew nothing. She was terrified. Locked in the cell, she could not sleep. She prayed David's words: " 'Out of the depths have I cried unto Thee, O Lord. Lord, hear my voice: let Thine ears be attentive to the voice of my supplications. Be not far from me, for trouble is near; for there is none to help. My times are in Thy hand. Deliver me from the hand of mine enemies, and from them that persecute me. In Thee, O Lord, do I put my trust: let me never be ashamed: deliver me in Thy righteousness. Bow down Thine ear to me, and deliver me speedily.' "

As she prayed throughout the night, she began to feel peace.

Deliverance came from a most unexpected quarter. It came from Herod himself! In the early morning hours, when the physician thought all of his efforts were in vain, Herod groaned and moved his head. A short time later, he opened his eyes and looked around. With great disappointment he said, "So I am still here! I have failed, even at that! I should have taken more poison."

His shocked physician asked, "Why did you do it?"

Herod replied dully, "Life wearies me, the pain consumes me, and there is no more pleasure for me. I am sorry to find myself alive."

The guard at the door heard all of this. He called his companion and said to him, "Go to the dungeon and get Sarah, if we are not too late."

It was not too late. When the cell door swung open, Sarah jumped to her feet. "Relax," the guard said to her, "we know you are innocent. The king took poison to kill himself. You can go to your room."

As soon as she had closed her door, she began to praise the Lord!

10

"I'm warning you! I'm not going to go on this way. You have to do something or I am going to take the whole box of poison. Nobody should have to suffer as I do. You talk to Joseph and come up with something, and you better do it soon. . . ."

Herod's voice trailed off as he spoke, but there was no doubt about the fact that he was filled with anger and frustration. His physician was about to answer; but, instead, he simply shrugged his shoulders. What did the man expect him to do? After all, he couldn't work miracles. Herod had closed his eyes and appeared to be asleep. His physician stood watching him for a while to make sure he was sleeping and not dying. Then he left the room to talk with Joseph.

"Well, he almost did it this time," said the physician. "I was afraid of that. He has spoken of the fact that Anthony and Cleopatra had taken the easy way out. If we don't do something, I'm sure that he will try again."

Joseph stroked his beard and appeared to be deep in thought. Would it have been such a loss if the poison had finished the job? But, no, his loyalty demanded that he do the very best for his king; so he said to the physician, "What can we do that we haven't done already? Nothing seems to be of any real help."

"We could try the hot springs near the Dead Sea. Many credit them with great healing powers, but I don't know if he would survive the trip. I wouldn't want to try."

"Wait a minute," said Joseph. "Don't be so hasty. That may be the answer. We have to try something. We could go to the summer palace at Jericho. Herod loves that place, and, from there, it is only a short trip to the springs. At least we will be doing something that will take Herod's mind off some of his problems."

"But Herod would have to be carried in a bed all the way, and the trip would take more than six hours."

"I can arrange for that. I will have a bed made to be carried by eight instead of four. It can be done. If we leave him to lie in bed here, he is gone.

We have nothing to lose."

"Well, Joseph, it is your decision," the physician said. "I will go along with whatever you decide. But let the king sleep as long as he can. When he wakes, you can talk to him."

Herod stirred many times, moaning as if he were having a bad dream, but it was late afternoon before he was alert enough for Joseph to talk to him. Since Joseph had had long experience dealing with Herod, he chose his words wisely. "There may be some healing for you in the hot springs near the Dead Sea; but that is beyond Jericho, and you are not strong enough to make the trip."

"Who says I am not strong enough? Did my physician tell you that? What does he know?" Herod stopped, and a far-off look came into his eyes. "Jericho, did you say? Oh, how I would like to see Jericho again! Is there really a chance that the mineral springs would help me?"

"Some say so," Joseph said.

"Then I say we go!" said Herod. It seemed that merely the thought of activity had revived some of the old fire. "We start today!"

"Not today," said Joseph. "The day is almost over, and we need time to construct a bed on which to carry you."

"You are right, Joseph. Tomorrow . . . we will go tomorrow. Now I will tell you who will go. There will be one hundred soldiers to lead the way, and one hundred to bring up the rear. I want one hundred of the servants from the palace to go along. Send a runner to the palace at Jericho so they will know we are coming. Now, let me rest. I am very tired."

Joseph left the room and closed the door. They would be leaving early the next morning. He said to himself, "Herod will never see Jerusalem again. I can see the end is near."

At dawn the procession left the palace in Jerusalem. Herod was being carried in an elaborate bed with a canopy overhead and curtains on the sides. "Pull the curtains aside and carry me by the Temple," Herod ordered. "I must see the Temple." One might have thought that he was a pious Jew wanting to worship God before undertaking the journey. This was not so. As the Temple came into view, Herod said softly to himself, "There stands a monument to my greatness. Even Solomon could not build what I have built! All of Israel should honor me, should thank me for what I have done. But what thanks do I get? They hate me!"

Then he told the guard beside him, "Order the process to halt!" The guard issued the order in a loud commanding voice, and the procession stood and waited, not knowing why. For a long time, Herod gazed at the

Temple. Time passed. It seemed as though he could not bear to leave its beauty behind. He seemed to be oblivious to the people around him. He would stay right here forever.

The guard realized what was happening and finally, embarrassed, said softly, "Oh, King. . . ." Herod stirred himself, aroused from his reverie, and said, "Yes, tell them to go on." The command was given, and the journey resumed.

They passed through the streets of Jerusalem and out of the eastern gate. As soon as Herod passed through the gate, he began to weep. "Oh, Jerusalem! oh, Jerusalem! I will never see you again. My golden city will belong to another." He wept bitterly.

As they continued down the road, the heralds proceeded the company to alert the people in the villages along the way that the king was coming. They blew their trumpets and shouted, "The king is coming! The king is coming!" Along the route, people lined the way; but there were no shouts of triumph, no waving of palm branches. They knew the king was old and sick; and, although they did not love or revere him, they would stand and pay their respects to the man who had ruled them for so long. The king was hardly aware of their presence; he did not care if they were there or not.

Sarah walked with Leah. Since the episode of the king's poisoning, Leah thought it best that she stay away from Herod. She did not know if the king had heard of the accusation against her, but it was not wise to take the chance. People had suffered a cruel death for much less.

"Today you shall see Jericho," said Leah. "It is a little paradise. You will smell the fragrance of the balsam trees long before we arrive. Although we accompany the king on a sorrowful journey, the beauty and fragrance of the city will be a delight to the heart."

In time, the city came into view. It was rightly called "The City of Palm Trees," and many sycamores and cypress trees could also be seen. The city, situated on a fertile plain more than twelve miles wide, was surrounded by high walls protected by four forts. Beyond it lay the Jordan River and the road to Arabia and Damascus. The city guarded the access to Jerusalem, and its strategic location made it the logical center for tax collection.

"And see that pile of stones?" said Leah, pointing to some ruins about a mile north of the city. "That is what is left of the old city of Jericho, the scene of Joshua's triumph."

Sarah knew the story well; the history of her people was part of her culture. Now, seeing this place made her a part of that history. But more than that, it reminded her that Israel had always faced enemies in the struggle for existence; and, time after time, God had intervened and had done the impossible. She thought about this and then said to Leah, "Perhaps the trumpets that announce the death of Herod will be the trumpet blasts that bring down the walls that hold us captive — our crushing taxes, a ruthless king."

Leah said to her, "I am not sure that the passing of Herod will mean our salvation."

"Nothing could be worse than what we have endured under this tyrant," said Sarah.

"I hope you are right," Leah answered. "We could use some peace and tranquility. 'Pray for the peace of Jerusalem.' " Sarah joined in the quotation, and they said together, " 'They shall prosper that love thee. Peace be within thy walls, and prosperity within thy palaces.' "

Finally they arrived at the palace; and, it was, indeed, a magnificent place with a huge reception hall. The walls were painted to resemble marble, and the floor was an intricate mosaic. On the south side was the sunken garden, and the courtyard was surrounded by large columns. There was an unusually large Roman bath, served by an aqueduct that brought water from springs ten miles away. It was a beautiful place!

Herod had survived the journey to Jericho, but he was much weaker and his maladies had increased. Plans were being made to carry him to the hot springs the next day, but many of the people around him were saying, "All the hot water in the world will not help that man!"

The king called Joseph to him that evening and said, "Joseph, Joseph, you have been a faithful servant to me; you are the only one I can trust. Keep the rest of those vultures away from me, even my sons. They know I am dying, and they are all after me like wolves. But I am going to do what I am going to do, and I don't need their help. But I *do* need you; I must finish my affairs before it is too late."

"Don't be so pessimistic," Joseph said to the king. "Many times you were given up for dead; and look, you are still here."

"This is different, Joseph; I know it. Next month, at this time, I will not be here. Now, this is what you must do. Call together all the leaders who are loved and respected by the people and have them meet with me here. I don't want the Sanhedrin, and I don't want those men who are hated by the people. I want elders, respected men, loved men. They may not want to come to Jericho, but tell them they must; this is a royal command. And I want them all! Next week!"

Joseph was surprised at this order. Generally, Herod had nothing to do with these men; he knew of their opposition to Rome, and he knew that he represented Rome to them. Joseph thought, *Can it be that the reign of terror is over? Perhaps Herod will do a great thing before he dies; perhaps he will listen to the true leaders of the people, the men who embody the hopes and aspirations of Israel.* Even as he thought these things, a nagging doubt crept into his mind. *Can a leopard change his spots?* Nevertheless, he had an order to carry out.

The next day Herod was carried to the hot springs. People came from great distances to bathe there and even to drink the water. The springs were located on the eastern shore of the Dead Sea, which they called the Salt Sea. It was the most remarkable body of water on earth, so salty and mineral rich that a person could float without effort.

It seemed a contradiction of terms, but this sea was almost thirteen hundred feet below sea level, the level of the Great Sea. It lay at the bottom of a large rift in the earth, and into it, the Jordan River and several other streams continually poured fresh water; but all this fresh water did nothing to dilute its saltiness which is six times as great as the ocean. In spite of the large volume of water entering, the level remarkably remained the same because of the rapid evaporation by the blazing sun. In addition, since this is a volcanic zone, gases continually escape from the surface of the sea. One would suppose that this would be a vision of hell; but, in fact, the scene was quite attractive. The sea was sparkling and smooth, surrounded by spring-fed lagoons. To the east, the pure white limestone walls of the Plain of Moab stand nearly a mile high above the sea.

The trip had been hard on Herod, and the physician told one of the attendants, "It will take a lot of healing just to make up for the distress he has suffered by being carried here. I fear this is a losing cause."

The king was in a foul mood. "Don't lift me that way! Put me down! Don't put me down that way! The water is too hot! The water is too cold! This isn't doing me any good! What are you trying to do? Kill me?"

Finally he called his physician. "Enough of this nonsense! This is doing no good. Is this all the help you have to offer? A fine physician you are! I should have gotten someone from Rome!"

"There *is* one more thing we might try," said the physician. "I cannot say that it will work, but I think it is worth a try. It may bring you some relief."

"I am willing to try anything if it will give me a little comfort and stop this dreadful itching. What is it?"

The physician answered carefully. "Some have gotten help by being lowered into a bath of warm oil. That, at least, should have a soothing effect."

"Then do it!" said the king. "Order the bath prepared at once!"

The oil was warmed to a comfortable temperature in a large tub. Carefully, slowly, the king was lowered into it. He let out a loud cry, so loud that it startled and frightened those who were standing by. Then he collapsed and would have slid under the oil if the attendants had not grabbed him. Someone cried out, "The king is dead! The king is dead!"

The king was not dead. Quickly they pulled him up out of the oil and laid him on a cot. In a short time, he revived and said weakly, "Enough! Take me back to Jericho, and let me die in peace."

Meanwhile, the honorable men were gathering from all over Israel. Most were not happy to be there; the invitations that brought them were commands, and it was even hinted that they would forfeit their lives if they did not comply. This did not produce an atmosphere of trust and confidence.

But there was hope. They had been told that Herod was about to die and wanted to consult with them. They were also told that Herod wanted only those who had the confidence of the people; "loved and respected men," had been his words. Perhaps this signaled a change. Perhaps there was reason to hope.

Sarah was passing by the sunken garden when her attention was drawn to an old man seated on a bench there. She had almost passed by, and then she turned to look again. She recognized him! It was Zadok, the elder of Ebba. She rushed to greet him; he recognized her immediately. "My daughter Sarah," he said with surprise. "Is it really you? How good it is to see you! Has the God of all mercy accompanied your steps with the dew from Heaven and honey from the rock?"

"Indeed!" said Sarah. "It is by the Lord's mercies that I have not been consumed." Then, without waiting any longer, "Have you seen my father?"

"Yes, I have. He came to visit Ebba a short while ago, and I am happy to tell you that he is fine, although he was worried about you. He misses you, but he is doing well. He is a strong worker, and everybody likes him; but I suppose you know he has a tendency to be lazy. Now he has no opportunity to be lazy," he said with a smile. "So I suppose you could say that he is a better man now than before."

"Do you expect to see him again soon?" asked Sarah. "I would like him to know that I am surviving my struggles with the help of God, and I miss him very much."

"I have no idea when he will come for another visit, but I am sure that he will be coming to Jerusalem for Passover. You could see him then. Where could he find you?"

"I do not know what my future holds," said Sarah sadly. "I do not know where I will be from one day to the next, my future is so uncertain."

"Life is uncertain for all of us," said Zadok. "Even in Ebba things are not the same. Do you remember the fellow who called himself Elijah, the fellow who talked about rebellion against Rome? His following is growing every day, but I see trouble ahead. I'm afraid that many are going to pay dearly for his rash actions and his lack of restraint."

Sarah was about to mention her involvement in Jerusalem, but thought better of it. Would Zadok understand? Would he approve? Was he condemning all such activity, or only the excesses? She had great respect for his wisdom. Perhaps she could find out without asking directly. "Do you think he is lacking in judgment?" she asked.

"More than that," said Zadok. "He is a hothead, and I am afraid that all Galilee will be in flames before he is through. I see no way to stop it. When that happens, many innocent people will be slaughtered."

"Herod is about to die," Sarah said. "Perhaps this will bring better days to Israel."

"When he is gone, others will take his place; and they will be no better than he is. No, our only hope lies in the Messiah."

Later, Sarah thought about this discussion. Should she sit and wait for the Messiah or should she take up the struggle for which Joash had so willingly laid down his life? Would his sacrifice be in vain? Then the thought came to her: *No doubt the fellow who called himself Elijah thinks he is being led by God. How can I be sure?* So she prayed, "Oh, Lord, guide my steps. My vision grows dim. Who am I? Am I Esther, or am I just Sarah? I need Your hand to guide me."

The king was back from his unsuccessful trip to the hot springs, weary, uncomfortable, discouraged, angry. As much as possible, the servants avoided him, anticipating an outburst of temper that would be disastrous to anyone within range. Herod knew his condition, he felt his life ebbing away; he felt the pressure of time upon him; and there were several things he had to do before he was through.

11

Early the next morning, Herod called Joseph into his bedchamber and said, "Now, listen to me carefully, and do exactly as I say. There must be no mistake."

"You ought to rest," Joseph said to him. "Don't talk now. That trip to the springs left you without strength. Wait until you are stronger; then we can attend to business."

"Wait? Wait? I cannot wait! My days are numbered; time is running out. I cannot wait; I must hurry. There are important things that must be done now!"

Joseph could see that it would do no good to try to change the king's mind. Herod was going to do what Herod was going to do, even if it killed him; so he said simply, "I am ready to carry out your orders."

"First," said the king, "go down and assemble all the elders and leaders in the great hall. Thank them for coming; be very kind. Tell them I am looking forward to talking with them later when I am stronger. Tell them to wait for me in the stadium. Then, listen to me carefully," he said with a sinister change in his voice, "have the guards escort them there and lock them in. Make sure the captain of the guards knows that none of them can leave the stadium . . . for any reason! Do you understand that?"

Joseph did not understand! "But I thought you wanted their advice; why lock them up?" he asked, trying to hide his surprise and disappointment. He had hoped that this meeting would signal an improvement in relations with the people. Now those hopes were dashed. He could see that Herod was not going to answer his question, so he started leaving to carry out the order. Now Joseph knew that trouble lay ahead; like a rudderless ship driven toward the rocks by a fierce gale, the affairs of the kingdom were rushing toward an unhappy conclusion.

Herod called after him, "Before you do that, send someone to summon my sister Solmay and my scribe. As soon as they arrive, bring them here; we have important business to attend to."

After Joseph had gathered the leaders in the assembly hall, he stood to address them. He felt like a hypocrite, like a traitor, but he had no choice. He looked at these men, leading men, honorable men, and wondered what Herod had in mind for them. He was sure now that Herod did not call them here to seek their advice. Something was wrong, but he had no choice but to go through with the performance.

"Honorable men and leaders of Israel," he began, but then could hardly find the voice to continue. Somehow he got through the brief speech. The leaders seemed puzzled, but not apprehensive. In due time, they were ushered to the stadium; but, when the gates were locked behind them, they sensed trouble.

Herod was lying on his regal bed, a pathetic, emaciated figure, struggling for breath. His sister stood beside the bed, Joseph was seated at the foot of the bed, and the scribe sat at a small desk with his scrolls and pens. Each of them was aware that this was going to be a momentous meeting, the passing on of power. The decision made by one man, a sick man at that, would affect the future of Israel for years to come.

Joseph had entertained hopes that, finally, some good decisions would be made. Herod's sister was not so hopeful; there was some reason that Herod wanted her to be here as a witness. Herod began his pronouncements: "I want things to be done exactly as I command, is that clear? You Solmay, and you Joseph, are witnesses. Make sure that the scribe is accurate and do not change anything; it is not your right to do so. As long as I am alive, I am the king and I will say what is to be."

Herod paused to gather up his strength. Joseph shifted uneasily in his chair. Solmay braced herself for what would follow such a stern beginning.

"First of all, about my sons. My oldest son, Antipater, shall have nothing. He is untrustworthy, he hates me, and has always been plotting against me. He thinks he shall be able to take the kingdom when I am gone. Well, he is wrong! He won't be around to take the kingdom! I hereby order his execution now, and I am going to seal it with my seal. It will be done tomorrow! Tomorrow! Do you hear? And don't say, 'We will wait, in the meantime, the king may die.' I want it done, and I want proof that it is done. Do you understand?"

Joseph understood. He understood that there would be no merciful conclusion to Herod's reign. He simply nodded his assent.

"Now the kingdom," said Herod. "It is to be divided into three parts." Joseph was about to speak, but the king held up his hand for silence. "Jerusalem and Judea will go to Arkus."

Joseph could not maintain his silence at this. "Haven't you made an error, oh, king? Your will says that Herod Antipas will be the king of Jerusalem.

Besides, Arkus is not equipped to be king. He is not wise, he is hated by the people, and there is sure to be a rebellion if he is chosen." Joseph suddenly stopped short; he had been speaking strongly, and he had no right to do so. Surely Herod would be offended.

But Herod firmly replied, "It shall be as I have spoken it! Write that down, scribe; the other will is no longer valid."

Joseph groaned to himself, "We are in for an uprising!"

Herod continued with his instructions: "Herod Antipas shall have Galilee and east of Jordan, and Herod Philip, the rest." Herod saw the puzzled, disappointed look on Joseph's face, and said, "Shall I tell you why I have decided this? No, perhaps I shouldn't." He lay silent, and for a while, Joseph thought he would say no more. Herod was debating in his mind whether he should disclose his secret or take it with him to the grave.

His arrogance would not allow him to keep it to himself; he had to tell. So he began, "I, myself, have built this great kingdom. I have built great cities; I have built the great Temple. Do you think I will let someone else move into what I have built and bask in the glory I have created? No! There will never be another king like me. No other ruler will rule this land as I have ruled it. I will go down in history, and there will be no other name mentioned with my name!" This venomous introduction exhausted him; he closed his eyes and was still. He had revealed his real character, the force that had driven his life, the ambition that had consumed him: He would not share his achievements with anyone, not even his sons.

After a long period of waiting, he opened his eyes, and continued, "Will there be weeping and mourning when I die?" He paused, waiting for an answer, but no one spoke. "Will there be rejoicing when I die?" Again he paused. Then he smiled wickedly and said, "I will tell you the answer. There will be weeping and mourning such as this land has never heard! You doubt this? Do you think the old king has taken leave of his senses? Oh, no! I now make a royal command! When I die, tell no one! No one! When I die, go at once to the stadium and order the soldiers to kill every one of those revered, honored men. Shoot them all with darts. Then tell all Israel that they are dead, and when the wail goes up from the land, say, 'And also, the king has died!' There will be weeping when I die."

There was a stunned silence in the room. "And my personal guards," demanded Herod suddenly, "will they rejoice when I am gone? When they thought I had been poisoned, did they rejoice?"

"No, they did not," said Joseph.

"What was their response? What did they do?" asked Herod.

"They tried to search out the one who had done the deed. They apprehended the girl, Sarah, because, at one time, she had talked of poisoning your wine."

"She spoke of that? She thought of that? And what has been done to her?"

Joseph was sorry that he had slipped in his effort to defend the guards. He had not been careful in his answers. Would his carelessness cost Sarah's life? But the king was waiting for his reply, so he said one word, "Nothing."

Herod said ominously, "When you get back to Jerusalem, see that she is dealt with . . . harshly. Now, all of you, leave me. I am very tired."

Those were the last words they heard him speak.

The next day, Leah and a group of servants prepared food for the men in the stadium. There was nothing unusual about this; they assumed that the leaders were to wait until Herod was able to see them. When they got to the stadium, the true situation became obvious. Guards unlocked the gates and carefully locked them after they had entered. Something was wrong here.

When Leah returned to the palace, she sought out Sarah and said to her, "Your friend Zadok is locked up with the rest of the men who came here trusting Herod. I fear for their lives; and, if this goes on much longer, I fear for the health of the other old men like Zadok."

Sarah replied, "Will his cruelty never end? Here I am, just a simple country girl, and yet he has already marred my life. He has caused the death of my friend Joash, and now the life of Zadok is threatened. Who knows how many he has bereaved, how many lives he has ruined?"

Sarah went out and sought a quiet place to pray; this was her only weapon. Prayer seemed so weak a response to the tide of evil issuing from Herod; but God had answered her prayers before, and she had to cry out for aid and protection to the only One who could be of help. So she prayed.

Herod lingered on for several days but never revived. The palace was filled with a strange sense of anticipation and uncertainty. The royal family, what was left of it, began to gather to wait for the end. When it was certain that the king would die at any moment, Joseph gathered the family to read the contents of Herod's will. First he dealt with the matter of the distribution of Herod's great wealth. Herod had willed a great chunk of it to Caesar Augustus, and special favors to Caesar's wife — he was an astute politician to the very end — but there was enough left to make all of them very wealthy.

Then he came to the matter of the kingdom. Herod Antipas fully expected that the kingdom would be his; the previous will had stated that, and accordingly, he had already made plans. In casual conversations with Joseph, he had indicated this, but Joseph had said nothing. He had decided to wait until the reading of the will. Now he could put it off no longer. When he read what Herod had decided, Arkus shouted with joy and surprise. Herod Antipas complained loudly and angrily; Herod Philip said nothing. Perhaps he could see the great violence this division would create, and he would rather sit in peace in his remote northern part of the kingdom.

When it appeared that Arkus and Herod Antipas were about to come to blows, Joseph stepped in between them and said, "Of course, none of this is final; the ultimate decision will have to be made by Caesar Augustus. Your argument here is useless; but, since Herod has designated Arkus, it is his responsibility to order the funeral. I would suggest that you set things in motion at once. I think that if the king does not die today, he will die tomorrow."

An elated Arkus went out to begin the funeral arrangements, and a grumbling Herod Antipas went out, already making plans to overturn the decision. The fight had just begun.

Herod finally breathed his last. His physician had been by his bed watching him. The fury and anger were gone; all that remained was a shriveled, empty body. The physician placed coins upon his eyes and pulled up the cover. Then he summoned Joseph.

Joseph was not surprised when he was called to the bedchamber. He asked, "Are you sure he is finally dead?"

The physician replied with great relief, "He is finally dead!"

Then Joseph turned to the few servants who were in the room and commanded, "I want no one to leave this room. This news must not get out until I take care of some very important business." And then, turning to the physician, he said, "Please stay here with them and see that no one leaves. My business will not take long."

Joseph rushed to the chambers of Solmay and her husband and knocked urgently at the door. When they opened the door and saw Joseph, they knew the news he was carrying.

"So it is finally over," said Solmay. "At last he has peace."

Joseph thought to himself — but did not say aloud — *Not if there is a God in Heaven!* Instead he said, "We must decide about the king's order to slay all those men in the stadium. This should not be done! Herod caused enough pain during his life; it should not continue after his death. We cannot alter his will — that is sealed with the royal seal — but this was a verbal order, and I say that we should reject it."

Solmay agreed. "I believe as you do. I, too, have been troubled about that. Please announce the king's death, and then go personally and release those men.''

The great massacre had been averted.

The news of Herod's death spread quickly through the palace. There was no display of sadness, but there was a prevading sense of relief. Herod had been king for thirty-seven years, the only king most of them had known. But his character was also known. In his early days, he had been a slave to his passions, and his lustful activities were known to all. Lately, as his illness progressed, these declined, but his cruelty did not; he was vicious to so-called friends and foes alike. He seemed to have no concern for what was right. He had been only evil.

In keeping with the Jewish tradition, Herod was buried the day he died. Arkus had determined that this would be the most elaborate funeral Israel had ever seen; perhaps it was. First came the professional mourners with heads shaved, wearing sackcloth, accompanied by flute players. Next came the casket, studded with precious stones, covered with purple. The dead king was dressed in royal robes with a diadem on his head and a crown of gold above it. A scepter was placed in his lifeless hand. The royal family surrounded the casket and walked with bowed heads.

Next came Herod's private guards, hundreds of them, followed by the whole army in full battle dress. At the end of the procession came five hundred household servants bearing spices. Sarah walked in this group.

The burial was at Herodium, south of Jerusalem near Bethlehem. This was a fitting choice because it was a notable example of Herod's passion to build. He had begun with a modest mountain and transformed it into a palace and fortress. The entire mountain was reshaped until it formed a cone. Two circular walls enclosed the top, and four watchtowers overlooked the surrounding territory.

The funeral procession made its way up the road that circled the mountain; and, with great pomp and flourish, Herod was buried. Then seven days of official mourning began.

There was official mourning but not heartfelt mourning. Too many people had felt Herod's wrath, too many enemies had been made. Most were happy to see him go.

Even the man who appeared to profit most from Herod's passing, his son Arkus, found it difficult to grieve properly. During the day he put on a sad face, but at night, there were undisguised sounds of loud laughing and wild parties. This unseemly activity was duly noted by those who did not want him to be king.

Jerusalem was beginning a new page of history.

12

After the funeral, Jerusalem was like a boiling pot. While it was true that Herod's will gave the rule to Arkus, it was also true that he had more enemies than friends, who were sure to challenge the will before Caesar; and, before Caesar Augustus made the decree, nothing was finally decided.

In the palace, things were even more uncertain. Who would occupy the palace? Would the new owner bring in new people? What would happen to the servants? These uncertainties, on top of the pressure of the events that had just transpired, filled the palace with tension. Fear had filled the palace when Herod was alive; this fear was gone, but no one was naive enough to expect peace to replace it. Even the lowliest servant expected a time of turmoil. What came to pass was more than they could have anticipated.

Sarah, too, thought about her uncertain future. If she had known that one of Herod's last commands was to take action against her, she would have been more than a little concerned. But she did not know, and her concern was only for her immediate future. She was worrying in vain, because someone was about to cross her path who would change the whole direction of her life.

One sunny morning, Sarah looked out of the kitchen door and saw a familiar figure. "No, it can't be!" said Sarah. "Yes, it is! It is Benazra!" As she ran out the door, she shouted, "Benazra, Benazra!"

"Oh, Sarah, I am so glad to see you," said Benazra, "I have been wondering how you have been. You look fine; you have grown."

"You don't know the troubles I have survived by the help of God," Sarah said. "And now, with the death of Herod, everything is uncertain for all of us."

"And do you still call yourself Esther?" asked Benazra with a smile.

At first she did not know how to answer. She did not know whether Benazra was smiling because he thought this was a childish dream she should grow out of, or if he was asking her to share a secret confidence. After a hesitation, she said, "At times. But at other times, I feel that it is a hopeless cause. I have lost some good friends in the struggle, and I wonder

65

if they died in vain. I would say now, just call me Sarah."

Then Benazra said, "I have some important business to transact with Joseph; but after I am done, I would like to see you again. Will you still be here?"

"I will make sure to be here when you come," Sarah said. "It has lifted my heart to see you again."

Benazra wanted to say more about his "important business," but he thought better of it. If he was unsuccessful, Sarah would be very disappointed. No, if he was unsuccessful, he would never tell her.

Benazra had known Joseph for a long time, and many of the rich things in the palace had been brought on his caravans. As they greeted each other, Benazra said, "Joseph, you look very tired. These last days have been very hard for you, haven't they?"

"Yes, they have. No one will ever know how hard some of the decisions have been. I have been caught in the middle of many conflicts, and I have been forced into many things over which I had no control. I have been made to pass on orders that have caused great harm. I stayed because things would have been much worse without me, and I believe I have done more good than anyone will ever know." He thought about telling of the release of the men in the stadium but changed his mind. Already, it sounded as though he was making excuses for his career in the palace, trying to unload years of guilt in one conversation; so he stopped and changed the subject. "Do you have something special to sell me?" he asked.

"No," said Benazra, "I have nothing to sell; I want to buy something from you."

"I can't imagine what that would be," Joseph said. "What do I have that you couldn't buy on the market at a better price?"

"I would like to purchase the freedom of the girl, Sarah," said Benazra. He watched Joseph's reaction; he did not know if there would be complications or a refusal. He hoped it would come down to a simple matter of the price.

"Oh, yes, Sarah!" said Joseph, knitting his brow. "I had forgotten about Sarah. One of the last commands Herod gave was that I should deal with her. At one time, she was under suspicion for the poisoning of Herod, and when Herod heard that she had actually talked about doing it, he told me to 'deal with her' when I got back to Jerusalem. You know what Herod meant," he said grimly.

"You did not intend to carry out that order, did you?" asked Benazra. The very thought of it frightened him.

"No, certainly not . . . not with the king gone. And even if he were alive, I would have found some way around it. I would not like to see anything happen to her. What are your plans for her?"

Benazra shifted in his seat; it was going to be hard to explain what he had in mind, but it did help to see that Joseph evidently held her in high regard. So he said, "I knew her for only a short while, just during our journey to Jerusalem; but I became fond of her. I felt sorry for her. That might have entered into it, but more than that, I saw ability and determination that is rare. I would not like to see her buried under adverse circumstances and impossible limitations. I guess I feel like a father to her."

"More like a grandfather, I would say," Joseph said with a laugh. "But I know how you feel; I understand. So what do you propose?"

"I could not take her with me; I am always on the move. And my motive would be misunderstood." The expression in his voice told Joseph that he had thought about this, considered it, weighed it; and, if he could have found a way to do it, he would have. But Benazra was right; he could not do that.

There was silence, and Joseph waited for Benazra to continue. When he did not, Joseph said, "So . . .?"

"I want her to have a fair chance at life. I also happen to think that she has a great deal to contribute to our nation. I don't think she will ever be the deliverer she thinks she is, but she has hopes and dreams that are contagious. I think she could even enlist me in her cause."

Joseph considered this and said, "You know that her cause is dangerous business in Jerusalem, and there is a good probability that it could cost her her life."

"I have thought about that, and it troubles me; but I am certainly not going to make the decision for her."

"So what have you decided?" asked Joseph. "You have evidently been thinking a lot about this."

"I would like to buy her freedom, and let her make her own decisions and live her own life. She is not afraid of work, and I believe she will find a way to the top in any situation. What do you say?"

"With all the changes we face here in the palace, I think I can make a deal with you. I might say that I do it with delight. Pay me the token price so I can enter it in the books, and the deed is done."

Money changed hands again. Sarah was free!

Benazra's heart was overflowing with joy as he sought out Sarah. He thought of different ways to break the news, but discarded them all. He was not good at dramatic performances. When he found her, he said without embellishment, "Sarah, I have just bought your freedom!"

At first, Sarah did not comprehend; this came as such a surprise. When the reality finally dawned on her, she did not know how to respond. There was no way for her to thank Benazra, and she could find no words that even began to express the feelings of her heart. After a stunned and embarrassed silence, with tears running down her cheeks, she said again and again, "Thank you, thank you, thank you!" There was nothing else to say.

Benazra covered her embarrassment by taking her hands and telling her, "Sarah, you are a true daughter of Israel, and I pray that the God of Israel will guide your feet in the ways of peace and bless your new life which begins today." Then he pressed a gold coin into her hand, the first she had ever had. Turning quickly, he walked out the gate, tears of joy running down his cheeks.

How Sarah cried, too!

"Leah, Leah!" Sarah kept shouting as she rushed to find her friend to tell her of her good news. She found her at work in the kitchen. By that time, Sarah was so excited that she was jumping for joy. When she tried to speak, the words poured out in such a torrent that Leah could not understand what she was saying. "Now take a deep breath and tell me slowly what you have to say," Leah said. The story came out in bits and pieces; but, when Leah finally understood what Sarah was saying, she began to laugh and cry at the same time. She hugged Sarah tightly.

"What are you going to do now?" asked Leah.

Sarah's jumping and shouting stopped, and a puzzled look crossed her face. "I haven't had time to think about that!" she said. "What *will* I do?"

"What do you want to do? For the first time, your life is your own. That is wonderful, because it means you can make your own decisions; but it also means that you alone are responsible for your mistakes, and mistakes are easy to make. Be sure you make right choices."

"I don't want to go back to Ebba," said Sarah thoughtfully. "My father is gone, and there is no work for me there. I really have no home to go to."

"You could stay right here and work in the palace. I'm sure they would take you as a paid servant."

"No, never!" said Sarah. "This is the one place I do not want to be! The halls are filled with violent memories. Whenever I pass the great hall, I think I can still see Joash with his arms bound behind his back . . . and the others . . . no, I wouldn't stay here."

Leah smiled and said, "Would it surprise you to learn that I'm not going to stay here either? The future is too uncertain in this palace."

"Could I go with you?" asked Sarah anxiously. "You have been like a mother to me. I would like to go where you go, and work where you work."

"You know, Sarah, I think that is wise. I would feel very uneasy leaving you behind; that troubled me every time I thought of it. Let us pray that God will open a door for both of us."

Benazra went about his business in Jerusalem. His merchandise was too expensive for common people, but in Jerusalem, extreme wealth was to be found in unlikely places. The palace of the High Priest was such a place. The display of wealth here rivaled any to be found in the city. Benazra had sold some of these treasures to them himself; and, although it was good business, it bothered his conscience to see the money given by the people as an offering to God used in such a way. But he had no choice about that.

Outside the gate of the High Priest's palace he met a rabbi he had known for a long time. "My friend, Simon, how are you?" asked Benazra with a hearty smile. "I am happy to see you."

"I am happy to see you too, Benazra, but I am not happy to see you going into that sinkhole where God's money disappears like water in a hole in the sand." Then he smiled broadly to let Benazra know that there was a strong bond of friendship between them. "But don't be mistaken, my friend, I do not direct my anger against you; I save it for the evil around me."

"You sound like Sarah," said Benazra. This completely puzzled Simon. "Sarah? Sarah? Who in the world is Sarah?"

Benazra was about to pass off the remark, but then he thought better of it. She was going to get involved, he knew that; it would be better for her to be involved with responsible leadership.

This chance meeting between two friends outside the palace of the High Priest might put Sarah's life in peril. But at the same time it could be the thing that would protect her from a violent death in the uprising that was beginning to spread like a black cloud over Jerusalem. Yes, Simon was the one who could help her.

Jerusalem was in transition. Arkus had to go to Rome to receive the approval of Caesar, but he was not the only one seeking the kingdom. In the meantime, he had the advantage and he intended to press it to the limit. He decided that he would install himself in Herod's palace and promised a fight to anyone who would seek to dislodge him. His coming precipitated changes in the palace staff. This was the time Leah chose to make her move.

The old Maccabean palace near the Temple had belonged to Herod, and, in his will, he left it to Herod Antipas. An opportunity opened for Leah to work at that palace, and she was happy with the prospect. Herod Antipas had asked the manager for the one in charge under Herod to remain in that position. He was aware of Leah's abilities and the job she had done in

Herod's other palace, so he invited her to come and talk with him about this opening. The man's name was Levi; and, according to Joseph, who knew him well, he was a good manager and an easy man to work for.

Leah went to see him, and met him in the great hall of the ancient palace. She was at once impressed by his cordial manner and his ready smile. "If we run an efficient operation here," he was saying, "we will have an easy job. If Caesar approves of the present arrangement, Herod Antipas will be in his palace beyond the Jordan, and he will not come here often. He does come for all the feasts — I am not sure he is a good Jew; I think he comes only for appearances — and the palace will have to be ready at all times. But most of the time, we will be on our own. We must be ready for the master, whenever he comes, though, even if he comes unexpectedly in the middle of the night."

Leah already knew what her answer would be. "I would be very pleased to work for you and help with this responsibility. May I ask one favor? There is a girl who has been a big help to me in Herod's palace; I would like to bring her with me. She is energetic and dependable, and, also, I feel some responsibility for her."

Levi nodded. "Fine, fine," he said, "bring her along."

This time it was Leah who came to Sarah bubbling over with good news. "Sarah, guess where we are going! We are going to the palace of Herod Antipas!"

"Oh, no," said Sarah, "I could never work for anyone in Herod's family. You go if you want; I will find something else. I never want to see another Herod as long as I live!"

"I understand how you feel," Leah said, "but consider this. It is the old Maccabean palace near the Temple. Think of all the history wrapped up in that building; think of the thrill it will be just to walk those halls. Certainly you would like to be a daughter of the Maccabees! Just to live in that palace would make you feel a part of God's deliverance. And if that is not enough for you," she added confidentially, "I learned something else while I was taking a tour of the palace. Since your friend Joash and the others were killed, the rest of the group have been meeting in the back courtyard. To hear them tell it, the movement is very much alive and growing."

"This is nothing less than the hand of God," said Sarah with amazement. "I have been praying about my involvement. I had almost decided that I should give it up, and now this! Yes, I will go with you."

When Arkus came to take up residence in Herod's palace, they made the move. It was quite a change. Herod's palace had been the most modern in every way; the Maccabean palace was old and well-used. To Sarah it was a reminder of the history she had learned, of the days when Israel was free, and God was their only ruler. She had hopes now that those days would return.

She was not the only one who entertained such hopes. The passing of Herod had revived expectations that this could be a reality.

The thought of Israel as a theocracy, not under the heel of Rome, stirred deep patriotic feelings. This was the subject of discussion and fervent hope of the group that met in the back court of the Maccabean palace.

When Sarah heard of the meetings, she decided to join them. Since she had not been invited, she waited around the back gate when it was time for them to arrive. The first few folks who came did not know her, but then along came some of Joash's friends who recognized her. "Sarah," they said in surprise, "what are you doing here?"

"I work here in this palace now," she said. Then she waited, hoping they would invite her to join the group for the meeting. Without hesitation, one of them said, "Come with us; I want you to meet Simon."

In the center of the group stood Simon. Sarah was introduced to him as the one who had been the contact for Joash in Herod's palace and had been his trusted friend.

Simon's response surprised Sarah. "I know who you are," he said.

"How could you possibly know me?" she asked. This seemed impossible to her; he must have confused her with someone else.

"Your friend Benazra told me about you," Simon replied. "I didn't expect to find you so soon. I welcome you into our group."

Sarah knew that she was in a group that understood her passion; she felt that her doubts about her mission were now all a thing of the past. The path ahead was clear, and it was a road that promised freedom for Israel. No sacrifice would be too great, even if she had to suffer the same fate that befell Joash.

Joash . . . that was what Simon was talking about just then. "The sacrifice of Joash and his fellows will not be in vain. The manner of their deaths was so horrible, so barbaric that every reasonable person in Jerusalem is filled with outrage. The flames of their martyrdom will light fires of freedom from Dan to Beersheba. We must keep the flame alive!"

In the discussion that followed, they decided that they would meet for a memorial to the martyrs on the next two Sabbaths in the Temple courtyard. The third Sabbath would be Pentecost, and multitudes from all over Israel, indeed from the whole world, would be in Jerusalem for the celebration. This would be their opportunity to share their vision and light these fires of freedom. As they prayed to the Lord for guidance and for His blessing, hopes ran high. A new day was about to dawn for Israel.

They could not possibly know how wrong they were. The sparks they were lighting now would not produce shining peace, but grief and struggle and tragedy.

The next Sabbath day, they met in the Temple courtyard. It did not take long for a crowd to gather around Simon, and the people listened intently as he recounted the story of the recent events. It was evident that the crowd shared the pain and outrage of which Simon spoke. Feelings ran deep. The next Sabbath, the crowd was even larger.

When Pentecost came, the city of Jerusalem was filled to overflowing. Every house was occupied by two or three families; sometimes relatives from other areas, sometimes strangers who needed a place to stay. Some lived in tents just outside the city. It was a time of fellowship, meeting old friends, making new ones, and a time for reinforcing the ties that bound scattered Israel together as a nation.

As Simon prepared to go to the Temple, he prayed for the wisdom of God for his great undertaking. This was a momentous day in the history of his people.

So many people thronged the Temple that it was difficult to move around. Simon made sure that he was surrounded by his friends, the inner circle of which Sarah was now a part, and the enthusiastic followers who had been recruited on the previous Sabbaths. He hoped that their enthusiasm would spread like a flame through the crowd.

A flame did, indeed, spread. Many had heard the story of the martyrs and loudly expressed their anger. Those who heard for the first time quickly joined in; and, if anything, were more outraged than the others. But Simon's purpose was not to stir up anger, but to lay a spiritual foundation for a revival in Israel. His theme was the same as it had been from the beginning: The Roman eagle on the Temple was a heathen idol that blocked the prayers of God's people so God could not hear. Before God's blessing could flow, the eagle had to come down; and, if Herod had been a true king of Israel, he would not have installed the eagle in the first place. At least, he should have agreed to its removal when they protested. "But what did the tyrant do?" asked Simon. "He burned at the stake all those who sought to purify Israel and open the doors of blessing for God's people."

The crowd responded enthusiastically with upraised fists and cries of anger. Simon raised his hands for silence and continued. "And who occupies the palace now? His son, born of a Samaritan woman! Can we expect a revival of God's blessing under his leadership? If we can, let him declare himself; let him tell us that he is willing to talk humbly in God's way. If not, we must do what we must do!"

A shout rang up from the crowd, they responded as one man.

The Roman general, Claudus, had been watching the proceedings from a tower in the fortress of Antonia which bordered the Temple area. He did not like what he saw. Before Simon began the spiritual part of his talk, Claudus left to report to Arkus.

Simon went on, "But the eagle on the Temple was not the only idol that hindered God's rich blessing. There are idols of the heart that are just as despised by God, and these, too, hold back His blessing." Then he pressed the people to examine their own hearts and remove the idols. He called for a spiritual revival. Now the response was not so enthusiastic; it was much easier to condemn the actions of Herod than to face personal sin and repent.

"Trouble at the Temple?" Arkus asked Claudus, as though he had been anticipating something. "What is it this time?"

Claudus related what he had heard of Simon's speech, and then added, "They are in an ugly mood; the whole thing could explode."

Arkus said patronizingly, "I'll tell you want to do. You go down and address them; tell them what they want to hear. Tell them that I agree with them, and we are going to have a holy nation from now on."

Claudus looked at him in disbelief. "How can you have a 'holy nation' as they expect? Respectfully, sir, how do you plan to accomplish that?"

"I don't! After the crowd has gone home, it will business as usual; but for now . . . just do as I tell you."

"Clever idea!" commended Claudus, and off he went to the Temple. When he came to the Temple courtyard, several of his soldiers went before, shouting, "Make way for General Claudus! Make way! He comes with word from Arkus."

Instead of parting to let the general through, the crowd surged around him. Simon raised his hands for silence and called out, "Give the general room. We will hear what he has to say!"

A voice rang out from the crowd. "We don't want to hear anything this Roman has to say!" The man who was speaking climbed up on a table and called out, "For too long we have been listening to what Rome has to say! For too long we listened to what the evil Herod had to say, and we do not want to hear what his son has to say! We have heard enough!"

Sarah tugged on Simon's sleeve and said to him, "I know that man. He calls himself Elijah and he comes from Galilee. Our village elder says he is a hothead and will bring the wrath of Rome down on all of us!"

While she was saying this, Elijah continued his tirade: "This land is our land; it was given to our fathers by God Himself. No Roman has the right to set foot on our soil, and certainly no Roman has a right to stand on the holy ground within our Temple gates. We should drive them out, just as Judas Maccabees did."

As he said this, he reached down, took off his rough sandal, and threw it at the Roman general with all his might. It caught the general squarely on the nose. In no time, blood began to pour down his chin and onto his tunic. The soldiers immediately drew their swords and cleared the way to the gate. As the general was retreating, he was pelted with a variety of flying objects, all coming from the direction of the followers of the so-called Elijah.

Simon called to Elijah sternly, "You have done a great disservice to our cause this day; your actions will cause many to suffer." Then he said to the people, "I would advise you all to leave the Temple and go to your homes and stay there. The punishment of Rome will be swift and terrible. Only the hand of God can avert bloodshed now!"

Elijah called out to the crowd, "Do not listen to that frightened old man. Do not flee like cowards. Where are those who are willing to stand in God's might and see the deliverance of the Lord?" As Elijah continued to lecture the crowd, Simon said to those around him, "Come quickly, all of you; we must leave right now. This is wrong. God is not in this."

The general was still bloody when he reported to Arkus. "What has happened to you?" Arkus asked in amazement.

"The crowd has been stirred up by a rabble-rouser. They are in open rebellion against Rome and against you!"

"Crush them!" said Arkus. "Crush them all! If we allow this to continue, no one will be able to stop it. Take your army and seal the gates so no one can escape and no one from the outside will be able to aid them; then march in and slaughter them all! Spare no one! I will teach them that they cannot treat me this way!"

In a short time, the army began advancing on the Temple. One of Elijah's followers saw them coming and shouted to him in panic. Elijah shoved his way roughly through the crowd and rushed out the rear gate and slid down the steep ravines behind the Temple just before the army arrived. They marched through the gates swinging swords as they came. A great cry went up from the trapped people; there was no place to hide, no way to escape. In a short time, no one was left standing; dead bodies filled the Temple court.

General Claudus returned to the palace and reported to Arkus, "We have done our job."

"Good," said Arkus. "that rebellious mob will remember this lesson for a long time."

Indeed, they would; they would remember it long enough to tell Caesar about it. The massacre in the Temple would help to bring Arkus down.

13

Even though Jerusalem was in turmoil Arkus could not delay his trip to Rome. He had no solid position until Caesar made his decision. It was a bad time to go, but he had no choice, so he traveled to Caesarea to board a ship for Rome. It would be a long time before he returned, and Judea would look different when he got back.

When Arkus left, the various factions in Israel knew that they would have to unite and form a common front against him. They decided to send a formal delegation to Caesar to present their case. Fifty men were chosen to represent them, and Simon was one of them. They carried a simple, but strong, message from the people: "We will not have this man to rule over us; we will never accept Arkus as our king." This was a bold, dangerous statement to make because they knew that Arkus could be as vicious toward his enemies as his father, Herod, had been.

Then they made their plea: "Let us be a nation governed by God. This is a part of our long history and it is essential to our culture. It will be to Rome's advantage to let us remain thus." As they made their plea, eight thousand Jews who were living in Rome stood outside to demonstrate their support for this declaration. All of this did not impress Caesar.

Herod Antipas also came to Rome, and he, too, had his supporters. Among these was Solmay, the sister of Herod. She had been at the bedside of Herod when he made the declaration that Arkus should rule Judea after him, but she was not in favor of this decision. Now she said so. Herod Philip was there too, not to protest the portion given to him, but to speak in support of Arkus.

Caesar listened to them all, but made no comment, asked no questions. He had made up his mind before they came. He spoke the word of authority, the word that could not be appealed.

"Herod's decision stands," he said. "I cannot please you all no matter what I do. I will do as I please. But there will be no King of the Jews; Arkus shall be called Ruler of the Jews. That is all. That is my decision. I have spoken."

The trip home was long and arduous, for most were carrying the heavy baggage of disappointment.

The man who called himself Elijah at first had no idea of the destruction he had caused; but, when he heard that three thousand had been slaughtered, he did not even feel a twinge of conscience. Instead he told the followers who remained, "God shall turn this event to our advantage; we will set all Galilee on fire." And then he set out to do just that.

With all the important people in Rome, the entire kingdom was left leaderless. Rebellion erupted everywhere. As Zadok had predicted and Elijah had promised, Galilee was a hotbed of insurrection and anarchy. Elijah went from town to town with his message, recruiting as he went. "The time of our deliverance is at hand," he would proclaim.

"You cannot fight the Roman army!" someone would shout.

"We will not fight the army," said Elijah. "We will overwhelm one city at a time; and, before they recover, we will strike another, and another. There are not enough Romans in all of Israel to contain us. If we miss this chance, if we fail to seize this opportunity, they will grind us into the dust. I would rather die on the field of honor than waste away as a slave to Rome. I will live free!" Many who heard him speak felt the same way, and the number of his followers grew day by day.

Sarah's father, Asher, became one of them. Things had not worked out as he had planned, although he had to admit that he had never been good at planning. Now there was nothing to plan; all decisions were made for him. There were advantages. The harvest, for instance, was no concern of his. He would eat whether it rained or not. But then, he wasn't sure that he liked the price of his security.

Nothing was his own — not even his life. According to Jewish law, he would go free on the seventh year. Did he look forward to this independence, or did he fear it? He did not know. Where would he go then? Would he try to find a place to start all over again? Alone? Surely Sarah had a life of her own by now. If he started over again, wouldn't the same thing happen again? *What am I going to do with my life?* he asked himself. He did not see any good answers.

Then one day while he was carrying a bag of grain through town on the way to the field, he saw a gathering of men and a speaker standing on the stump of a tree. *That's Elijah,* he thought. *I remember the time he came to Ebba and harangued us about Herod. I guess he is still at it.* Curiosity led him to the edge of the crowd, but soon he was listening with more than passing interest. His life was empty, like a plowed field awaiting the sowing of the grain. It was even more vulnerable to the sowing of weeds.

Elijah had delivered his oration with fire and passion. Asher debated what he had heard. He had nothing here! If he went with Elijah, at least he would be involved in a grand crusade. What did he have to lose? He was bothered by something unsteady about Elijah. "He could get us all killed," said a small voice within him, so he picked up his bag. But now it seemed to be twice as heavy. He dropped the bag at his feet and made his decision: He would cast his lot with Elijah. "I hope this means freedom for me, and for Israel," he said with a touch of political fervor.

In time, Elijah had gathered a small army around him. After a series of minor skirmishes, he announced to the men, "Now we are ready to begin our fight for freedom. Our first target will be the rich city of Sappo. The riches there are our riches; we will take and claim that which is our own. We outnumber the Roman garrison there, and we will enter the city before the morning light. At the rising of the sun, our swords will flash red with Roman blood, and the city and all that is in it will be ours. God will give us a great victory, and the fear of us will drive the Romans back to Rome."

They approached the city of Sappo according to plan, and they entered the city according to plan, but the battle was not as easy as they had anticipated. The Romans did not flee in fear, though they were outnumbered as Elijah had said. By noon, the battle was over, and the Romans who did not flee were killed. Elijah marched at the head of a victorious army and he led them to the palace. There they looted everything of value and set the palace on fire. As the flames leapt to the sky, Elijah proclaimed in a loud voice, "Today we light the beacon of freedom that shall spread over all Israel. All the palaces of the rich shall be burned, and the wealth shall be shared equally by all of us. We are now free people."

But some of the people were "freer" than others; some of the men who followed Elijah were thieves and robbers, and some were completely without discipline. For the rest of them this was not the sweet freedom they had anticipated. Violence was everywhere with quarrels and fights about trivial matters; and, Elijah, he who had set himself up as the ruler, did nothing to curb it. In fact, in many ways, he began to act like the rulers he despised and began to do the things that he had preached against so vehemently.

Asher became disillusioned with the whole matter and thought of leaving, but he had no place to go. He could not talk to anyone about this because he would be treated as a traitor, and that was not a happy prospect. So he said nothing and stayed.

One day Elijah announced that they were going to Jericho to destroy the palace there. "It is a symbol of the oppression by the rich," he explained. "It was built by Herod, and it will be destroyed by Elijah." Somehow, in his proud mind, that made them even.

They took the road that followed the Jordan River. When they came to a town, they took what they wanted. The local people would loudly protest, "We are Israelites, as you are. Why are you doing this to us?" To this Elijah's men would reply, "We are your liberators. You must help support your liberation."

They arrived at Jericho from the north. Asher had no idea that Sarah had been there in the palace; he had no idea that Zadok had been held captive in the stadium; it was just one more city to him.

Again the treasures of the beautiful palace were looted, and what couldn't be carried away was smashed. This, too, disturbed Asher. It began to appear to him that Elijah's army enjoyed destruction more than freedom. They always left a trail of ruin and misery behind them.

They returned to Sappo to share the loot they had taken along the way. This is what they called freedom — freedom to take what you wanted, to do what you wished, to take orders from no one, to be accountable to no one. What was happening under Elijah was happening all over Israel. Wherever a leader could gather a large enough following, he would set himself up as a ruler, and one even proclaimed himself king. They never stopped to consider that Rome would not allow this kind of activity to go on forever. Judgment was delayed, but it could not be avoided. Sooner or later, they would pay the price.

The governor of Syria was the highest Roman official in that part of the world; and, in the absence of authority in Israel, he decided to take command. He came with an army, and the first place he attacked was the city of Sappo. Elijah and his unruly mob were no match for the invading army. In a very short time, the city fell and Elijah and the rest of the leaders were captured and placed in chains. Then the Roman general commanded that all the inhabitants of the city — men, women, and children — should be sold as slaves. Asher was one of them. He went with the group to be sold in Damascus.

The Roman army proved to be efficient and irresistible, and they swept away all opposition before them. When they arrived at Jerusalem, the unorganized resistance crumbled under the full weight of Roman might. There was much destruction and much loss of life, and when it was over, the Romans were again in full control. Then they began the roundup of the ringleaders, the army fanning out through the whole country and capturing those who still remained at liberty. Then swift and cruel Roman justice exacted its toll. From one end of Israel to the other, crosses appeared, and two thousand were crucified. Thus they broke the back of armed resistance; thus they silenced the voices raised for freedom; thus they crushed the opposition. They called it *Pax Romana,* Roman Peace.

14

It took Arkus a long time to return to Jerusalem. It always took a long time to journey from Rome because ship schedules were uncertain, wind conditions unpredictable, and emergencies always expected. In addition, Arkus was not anxious to get embroiled in the minor war that was going on. The situation was confused; at times, his own soldiers fought the Romans, although, technically, they were on the same side. To play it safe, he decided not to return until the Syrian general Varus had completed his campaign and wiped out the troublemakers.

When he did return, the marks and scars of the conflict were everywhere. The opposition had been put down, at a great price. There was also a sullen resentment among the people. Some of this resentment was transferred to Arkus. After all, he was the representative of Rome, and he had just returned with the blessing of Caesar, even though the people had made it clear that they did not want him.

Jerusalem had hoped that life would be better without Herod, but they soon learned that Arkus was devoid of political skills and ill-equipped to govern. He was ruthless, and his wrath fell indiscriminately on those who displeased him for any reason. Again Israel groaned under oppression.

One Passover, Herod Antipas came to Jerusalem sooner than he was expected. Levi had tried in vain to contact Simon to tell him that they could not have their meeting in the back court. Then the thing Levi feared came to pass: Antipas saw the group gathering. He called Levi and demanded, "Who are these people? What are they doing here?"

Levi feared that a direct answer would cost him his job, but he saw no way out. He explained that Simon was one of the men who had gone to Rome to ask that Arkus not be allowed to rule. To Levi's surprise, Antipas said, "I would like to meet these people. At least we have one thing in common — we know that the rule of Arkus will ruin us all."

Levi took Antipas to the group and introduced Simon. Antipas appeared to be very impressed and gave a short speech expressing his support for their activity. "What Arkus is doing is wrong. I am sure that if Caesar Augustus knew of his actions, he would not approve. I am sure that he would remove him, and install someone who had the interests of Israel at heart. I warned him that this would happen if he approved Arkus, but he didn't listen to me."

Antipas left the clear impression that he would support an appeal to Caesar for the removal of Arkus, and the implication was also clear that he thought he was the one best suited to take his place. After his speech, like a good politician, he went around greeting the people. When he came to Sarah he said, "Haven't I seen you before? Weren't you at Jericho?"

Sarah was surprised that she should be noticed, and more surprised that Antipas had remembered where he had seen her.

Sarah replied, "Yes, my lord, I was in the household of your father, Herod."

"And where are you now?" he asked.

"I am employed by Levi, and I work here in the palace."

"Good," said Antipas diplomatically, "We need more young people like you who care about our nation. I am glad that you are working for me."

When Antipas left, Simon told Sarah, "I would not trust everything he says; he always looks out for his own interests. Keep that in mind."

Antipas worked behind the scenes, and his labor was effective. His words of encouragement had firmed up Simon's resolve to take some kind of action. When Antipas talked privately to the other leaders, the priests, the Levites, the Pharisees, the Sadducees, each group felt that this was the time to get rid of the capricious tyrant. His conversation with the Herodians took a little longer. Traditionally they supported any appointment made by Caesar, but their patience with Arkus had been strained to the breaking point, so they finally agreed.

Antipas remained in the background, but his advise was sought. Throughout all of this, he presented himself as a congenial, wise, and interested advisor, concerned only with the well-being of Jerusalem. He did not reveal the fact that his own lifelong ambition had been to be proclaimed king of the Jews.

Antipas suggested that Simon be the one to make the presentation to Caesar. "You see," he said, "he appears to speak for the common people. This will appeal to Caesar, especially when the whole religious community stands with him." Because it was the suggestion of Antipas, they all agreed. Simon was happy to comply. The delegation set out for Rome again to meet with Caesar. This time their expectations were higher than the previous time; they were there alone, unchallenged, to present their case.

The city of Rome had a reputation that was not at all flattering. This city, capital city of the world, was known for its immorality, frivolity, and fancy dress. One might reasonably expect, then, that Caesar, the ruler of it all, and the ruler of most of the world, would be dressed finer than them all and live in the greatest luxury. This was not the case. The ruler ate simply; the people went to wild excess. While their ruler believed in chastity, the people indulged in their orgies. While their ruler wore a homespun garment, the people heaped on jewels and gaudy ornaments.

Caesar met with them in his own house on Palatine Hill. It was not a palace by any stretch of the imagination; it was a house, an average house with a modest portico and plain courtyard. Caesar was not wearing royal robes, but what he always wore, a toga woven by his wife, Julia. He was just finishing his main meal for the day — a slice of course bread with some pickled fish, and a pint of wine — that was all! This man, the most powerful man in the world who, by himself, without consultation with others, made decisions to affect the history of nations, had long been an advocate of the simple life. He urged this on the citizens of Rome, but his example was shunned.

However, Simon especially, felt at home in these surroundings. He could see that Caesar looked upon him and his simple style with affinity and approval. This gave him hope for a favorable outcome and filled him with quiet confidence as he prepared to make his presentation. With his gray hair and long beard, he looked like an Old Testament prophet; his manner was mild, his speech measured and calm. Caesar was surprised at this; he was used to lawyers who thought of themselves as the great orators of the world and Caesar's court as the stage on which to perform. With a wave of his hand, Caesar directed Simon to proceed.

Simon unrolled his scroll several inches, and then began: "Most excellent Caesar Augustus, the cry of the entire nation of Israel comes to you now. It is the cry of the High Priest in the Temple, the farmer in the field, the fisherman in his boat, and even the women and children in their homes. We cannot live any longer under these conditions. We have come to Caesar for relief, for justice. We want you to know that Arkus is a disgrace to Rome; he tarnishes the honor and reputation of your kingdom."

This made an impression on Caesar. If these words were true, that would be enough. The honor and reputation of Rome mattered more than anything else, expecially some petty ruler of a far-off kingdom.

Simon continued, "Before he was even appointed, he had proved himself unworthy in our eyes. Arkus shamed us all at the death of Herod. We honor our dead, and mourning for the dead is an important part of that honor. We have rules about this to instruct the ignorant, so that we as a people will not be shamed by the careless conduct of any at the time of death.

"Throughout the mourning period, we all heard loud parties and dancing and laughing and merrymaking coming from his palace. One would have thought that there had been a great victory over an enemy, not the death of a father. This was a shame to us, an affront to decency. It is true that the disturbance in the Temple had its roots in our anger over the young men Herod burned at the stake. It would have been nothing more than that — a show of anger at the deed done and over — but then the latent anger and hatred for Arkus broke loose like a flood. It was no longer an expression of sorrow over our loss, but a demonstration of our fear that more of this was to come. Then, as you know, Caesar, Arkus responded with anger, filling the Temple with dead bodies, men, women, and children, and not only from Israel, but visitors at the Passover from every nation on earth. This is a shame to Rome.

"I will not impose on your good grace to list the long account of his cruel and inhuman actions against all people, actions that make a mockery of Roman justice and of simple fairness which can be found even among the barbarians who know no law. We appeal to you, Caesar, help us." Simon slowly rolled his scroll and stepped back. The others who had come with him stood silent, impressed.

Caesar said, "You shall have justice. I will consider your plea." He was embarrassed; this man Arkus was giving Rome a bad name. He agreed to the petition and made the decree. Arkus was to be removed from office and banished to Gaul in disgrace. Caesar would make a new appointment. The delegation returned to Israel with hopeful and rejoicing hearts. At long last, someone had listened to them.

All Jerusalem was rejoicing when Arkus left; they felt no sympathy for him in his banishment. He deserved it, and more. Arkus would never sit in Jerusalem again. The rejoicing continued until they heard who Caesar had appointed to take his place. He had chosen a minor Roman official to whom he owed a political favor. He would prove to be no better than those he replaced.

The man's name was Pontius Pilate.

15

Herod Antipas came from a large, loosely knit family. Since his father had ten wives, each with children, things got complicated at times. A number of them were named Herod, which confused anyone who was only casually acquainted with the family. Two had the name Antipas, and two, the name Philip; Salome was a name common among the women.

Antipas had a brother named Philip who had been disowned by Herod and hence was not given a part of the kingdom. This suited him fine; he did not care for the responsibility, or the antagonism of the populace that went along with the job. He had a few business enterprises, but for the most part, he was happy to live off the portion of the family fortune that came his way.

Philip had a wife named Herodias, and, whereas he lacked ambition, ambition was her consuming passion. To put it bluntly, she aspired to be queen of all Israel. That did not seem possible, but this scheming woman would never admit any possibility of failure. Often, when Antipas was in Jerusalem, he would visit his brother; but even the casual observer could see that his interest was centered more on his brother's wife than on his brother.

Antipas had come to Jerusalem on business and decided to use the occasion to visit Philip. Along with him, he took some of his own people from the palace; this included Levi, Leah, and Sarah. This was Sarah's first visit to Philip's palace, and a surprise awaited her there. After taking care of their responsibilities with Antipas, Leah and Sarah went to the low building in the back that housed the servants. In the courtyard near the gate Sarah thought she saw a familiar figure. Unsure, she decided she was mistaken, but then she looked again.

It can't be! she said to herself. *It could be! It must be Alex!* She was about to call out when he turned toward her. His reaction was the same as hers had been. He glanced at her casually, started to turn away, then looked again. Years had passed since they had seen each other, but he knew her. He let out a shout, "Sarah!" and came running toward her. "Is it really you?"

"I should ask the same question," said Sarah. "Is it really you?" For a moment they stood awkwardly looking at each other. They had known each

83

other for only a few days. Even if they had had a firm friendship, there had been no contact between them since that time; and people change.

Alex broke the silence. "Sarah, I have thought of you often. At first, I was concerned for your safety, and I tried to pray to your God for you. I'm afraid that didn't work. Then I wondered if we would ever meet again. I had given up hope, but then Benazra brought me news about you, and" — he stopped abruptly — "I wonder — did you ever think of me?"

The words were tumbling out of Alex unguarded, and now he felt he had been too direct, too pressing. Perhaps she did not share his interest. How could she? He feared that he had placed her in an embarrassing position.

Sarah saw his awkwardness and gave him a smile that told him more than she was at first willing to say in words. "I am free now; Benazra bought my freedom, and gave me a life of my own. I was so young when we first met, and so many things crowded into my mind. At first, I was afraid of you, and then I felt that I owed you my life, and then I felt I loved you. I told myself that could not happen so quickly. Then I told myself that you are a Gentile, and I could never consider you — I told myself that, but my heart would not listen. Once, I found someone who . . . sometimes I wonder if I liked him because he reminded me of you."

She paused; now *she* had said too much. It is dangerous to open your heart too quickly, but she could not help it. So she smiled quickly and said, "I am glad to see you again, Alex."

Just then, Leah called for Sarah and their conversation was interrupted. How much more she wanted to say! So many questions she wanted to ask! Was this the Lord's doing? What did this chance meeting mean? Why did she feel as she felt now?

"Leah, Leah!" she said when they were alone. "The man I was talking to when you called me . . . that is Alex, the one who befriended me on the way to Jerusalem, the one who saved my life."

Leah smiled knowingly and asked, "Why are you all aflutter, Sarah? What is so special about Alex?"

"I don't know," replied Sarah. "I don't know. I am so full of questions. I had only a few minutes to talk to him. I don't know why he is here, or where he is going. I don't know if I will see him again, but I think I will die if I don't! Oh, Leah, what is happening to me?"

"Right now, we are going to work, or something will happen to both of us that we will not like," replied Leah. Sarah went to work, but her mind was elsewhere.

That night when the work was all done, Sarah lay on her bed and thought about what had happened to her that day. Seeing Alex had stirred up memories that she had tried to put out of her mind — not memories of him, but certainly memories of the wrenching experiences of that time when she knew him. She remembered again the pain she had felt when she said good-bye to her father; she remembered the fear and anxiety that had filled her on the journey to Jerusalem; she remembered standing in the slave market and then leaving for Herod's palace. All of these were dreadful memories, and Alex was tied to them. Now that she thought of it, Alex was always the bright spot, the happy memory.

But that was past. Whatever she felt then could not explain what she felt now. He did seem sincerely interested in her, didn't he? What was it he had said? She went over the entire conversation in her mind.

But the old doubt arose again, the barrier that first separated them: He was a Gentile. There was no doubt in Sarah's mind that God came first for her; there would be no lasting happiness if she walked a path that was not pleasing to the Lord. Still . . . So she prayed, "Oh, Lord, Thy word is a lamp unto my feet and a light unto my path. I will rest in Thee, Oh, Lord, and wait patiently for You, for You will give me my heart's desire. I know that You will withhold no good thing from those who walk uprightly."

As she lay on her cot, she thought hopefully, *Boaz was Jewish and Ruth was a Gentile, and yet God in His goodness brought them together, and from this family came our great king David. Who knows what God can do?*

The next evening after work was done, Leah and Sarah walked through the garden to a courtyard near the back gate. Many of the servants and workers were gathered there to enjoy the cool of the evening and rest after a day's labor. Leah and Sarah decided to join them. Almost immediately they saw Alex on the edge of the group, and Sarah said to Leah excitedly, "There is Alex! What should I do?"

Leah said, "I will give you the same advice that Ruth's mother-in-law gave her. 'Sit still, my daughter.' Let him make the first move; if he has any interest in you, he will." The mention of Ruth made Sarah's insides flutter again.

"If he does come over," Sarah said, "please don't leave me! I feel so nervous." To herself she said, *I hope he doesn't see me. What will I do if he sees me and ignores me? I don't know what I want!*

Her indecision did not last long. Alex saw her and broke into a beaming smile that melted away all of her worries and put her at ease before he even got to her.

"Sarah, Sarah!" he called. "I have been trying to find you. I didn't know where to look. Why are you here?"

"First," said Sarah, "I want you to meet Leah, who has been like a mother to me."

Sarah watched to see what Leah's response would be. She trusted her judgment, and thought deep inside, *Oh, I hope she likes him!*

Friendly greetings passed between Leah and Alex, but as soon as it was politely possible, Alex turned his attention back to Sarah; so Sarah told him, "I am working for Herod Antipas. He is here to visit his brother and brought us along. Why are you here?"

Alex replied, "Do you remember that I told you I wanted to work as a silversmith? Well, I have been, and I have been doing so well that I have purchased my freedom. Now I am managing the business for Philip, who used to be my owner. I am happy with this arrangement; it is good for both of us. How long will you be staying here?"

Sarah could sense that he did not ask that last question out of idle curiosity; this filled her with hope and expectation. Was God answering her prayer? Leah answered the question, "We will be here for a few more days, at most. We must be ready to move when the orders come."

Sarah and Alex were so intent on sharing their experiences that they hardly noticed when the music began. There were two men with shepherd's pipes, two with harps, and others with drums and cymbals. Then they began to sing together, folk songs and joyful psalms. The music turned lively, and several began dancing. It was a time of good fellowship and joy. Then a young girl pushed her way through the crowd. She was dressed like the others, but there was a sultry beauty about her. Alex said to Sarah, "That's Salome, the daughter of Philip and Herodias. She is not supposed to be down here. If her mother catches her down here, she will be in trouble."

Salome said something to the musicians, and they began to play a sensual desert dance. Salome casually kicked off her sandals and took the ornamental combs out of her hair; it fell like a dark cascade around her shoulders. The evening shadows had darkened and a large torch illuminated the scene. The flickering light made the young dancer a dramatic figure.

She began to dance slowly, as though she was coaxing the music to follow her into forbidden realms. With a flourish, she pulled off her belt and cast it to one side, letting her robe swirl seductively about her as she turned. She seemed to move with an animal passion, and the intensity and tempo of the music increased to match it.

Alex abruptly turned his back on the performance and said to Sarah, "That is a disgusting exhibition of sexual temptation. She knows what effect she is having on the men. See how they stare at her! And yet, if one of them so much as speaks to her, she is cruel and threatens to use her power against them. Her purpose is only to tempt and to tease. I suppose it gives her a feeling of control over those in her spell."

Sarah wanted to turn away, but could not; she was fascinated, spell-bound. She could not believe her eyes. It was unthinkable that a young woman should be so brazen, so indecent, so frankly tantalizing. And this was not some slave girl dancing for some coins; this was the granddaughter of King Herod — royalty! How could she do this?

As the dance was reaching its climax, it was abruptly halted by a demanding, commanding voice that rang out above the music, "Salome — stop that! Come here this minute!"

The music stopped in midnote, and everyone turned to see who had called. It was Salome's mother, standing on the steps of the garden over-looking the scene. Her eyes blazed with fire. She had a regal appearance about her. Her beautiful robe was fastened with a jeweled belt. Her hair was piled high on her head, held in place with combs of silver and gold, studded with gems. As Herodias stood there, Salome appeared to be a pale copy of her regal beauty.

Salome gathered up her sandals and belt slowly, deliberately, trying to make it appear that she was not under her mother's thumb, but at the same time being careful not to offend her mother further. As they walked through the crowd, her mother said in a low voice, but so distinctly that all could hear, "You are a shame to the family name!" As the girl walked by, the flickering light of the torch cast her shadow, larger than life, upon the opposite wall, sending a shiver down Sarah's spine. This caught her by surprise. She had never seen this girl before; she did not know her. She disapproved of what she had done, but that would not account for the ominous feeling that overwhelmed her as the shadow moved across the wall — as if a dark shadow could be an omen of a dark event!

Later that night, Herod Antipas was lying in bed going over some of the accounts of his kingdom when he heard a quiet knock on his door. It was so quiet that at first, he was not sure he had heard it at all. As he hesitated, it came again: rap . . . rap. He thought that perhaps it was one of the servants who had forgotten something, so he called out, "Come in." The door opened only a little way, and a figure quickly slipped inside and closed the door. Antipas, sensing danger, was about to call out for help, but before he could, the figure stepped into the ring of light cast by the lamps. Antipas caught his breath and then exclaimed, "Herodias! What are you doing here at this time of night?"

"Am I not welcome?" said Herodias with a smile.

"What do you want?" asked Antipas.

"I will tell you in a moment, but first, am I welcome?"

Now Antipas understood what was going on. On previous visits, he had noticed that she had paid considerable attention to him. On several occasions at supper or in the evening as he and his brother talked, he had observed her watching him with obvious admiration. Then he found himself watching her, at first, almost unconsciously, but then on purpose. She was, indeed, beautiful. Thoughts now raced through his mind. Things were not going well with his own wife. Even his brother remarked that most of the time he left her at home. But should he become involved with his brother's wife? No, he should put that out of his mind. Then, halfheartedly he said, "You shouldn't be here."

Herodias answered coyly. "Then send me away."

Antipas hesitated and said nothing while Herodias watched him closely, waiting. When no reply came, she said, "See, you feel as I do. It will do you no good to fight it. We were made for each other."

She did not give him time to reply, but kicked off her sandals, just as her daughter had done in the courtyard. Then she pulled the ornate combs out of her hair, just as her daughter had done, and sat on the chair near the bed, watching for his reaction.

Finally, Antipas said, "There is no future in this. I have to think of my position in my kingdom."

"That's exactly what I am thinking about," said Herodias, "and there is a future in it — for both of us."

"What do you mean?" asked Antipas.

"You need a wife with ambition, and I need a husband with ambition. Philip will never amount to anything, and that doesn't bother him a bit, and your wife, Doris, stands in your way. You will never climb the path to greatness with her at your side. You will end up on the other side of the Jordan with the peasant Galileans! That should not happen to you. You are better than that. Even Herod knew that, but in his last days, when he was out of his mind, he changed his will. But he knew it, and if he had stayed with his first decision, Caesar would have approved it."

"It does no good to go over all of that now. That is all past and gone; we can't change it," said Antipas with resignation.

"Who says we can't change it?" said Herodias. "Don't you realize that you were born for greatness? All you need is someone by your side who believes in you and will encourage you. You need a wife who won't stand in your way."

"And I suppose you are that person," said Antipas.

"What do you think? Can't you see the future we could have together?"

"No, I can't see it. What can you see?" he coaxed.

Herodias leaned forward with her elbows on her knees, looked at Antipas, and said with a twinkle in her eye, as though she were a girl telling some hidden secret, "I see you as king of all Israel, and . . ." — she leaned back again and stretched out her legs in front of her — "and I will be the queen!"

Antipas was silent, thinking, *She really means this! Would this be possible?* Then he smiled and said, "So you want me just because you think I can make you queen?"

Herodias smiled her most beguiling smile and said, "You know better than that. Don't tell me you haven't felt it, too. I have seen you watching me. I can read your eyes."

"What about Philip?"

"He'll get over it," said Herodias with a shrug. "Don't worry about him."

"What about Doris?" asked Antipas.

"Send her back to her father; she will probably be happy to go. She is not made for this kind of life."

"What about Salome," asked Antipas, trying to think through all the ramifications of such a large decision.

"She comes with me," said Herodias. "She admires you; she says you look like a real king."

Herod Antipas was pleased with that; he had seen the little girl blossom into a young woman, and some of the thoughts he had about her would be better left unspoken. Herodias knew this and planned to use it to her advantage if the occasion should arise. Herod Antipas was deep in thought. She allowed him a moment to savor all of the possibilities; then she broke into the silence and said, "Well, aren't you going to invite me to stay the night?"

Herodias thought that no one had seen her slip into Antipas's chamber, but she was wrong. She had been seen.

The next evening, it was Alex who heard a knock at his door. He was working on a silver piece and did not look up from his work as he called out, "Come in." The door swung open, and then closed. Alex expected some kind of greeting from his visitor, and, when he heard none, he turned to see who it was. There in the shadows stood Salome. After a tense silence, she was the first to speak. "You turned your back on me when I danced. Do you find me that unattractive?" she asked with mock concern.

"You know you are attractive," said Alex. "That's the trouble — you know it, and you use it to tempt and lure. That's not fair to the men who watch you, or to yourself either."

"So, you are a priest to lecture me, are you? Perhaps you have no blood in your veins, and you are embarrassed about that!" Salome gave him a haughty look, and without being asked, sat down in the chair opposite him.

Alex felt uneasy about this; since she was the daughter of the man who employed him, she could make trouble for him if she chose. He did not want to anger her, neither did he want to encourage her, so he asked in a calm voice, "What are you doing here? You will be in trouble if your mother finds you here."

"I just wanted some company. I get so lonely all by myself in my room." She put on a sad face to evoke pity, and then she pouted a little. She had practiced this look and thought it would be irresistible.

Alex was on guard and said to her in an offhand way, "You are wasting your time here; I am not your type."

"You don't even know me," said Salome, enjoying the challenge. "So how can you say you are not my type. Besides, that's for me to decide. You are Greek, aren't you?"

"Why do you say that?" asked Alex.

"Because you look like a Greek god, and I think I like Greek gods," said Salome with a practiced demure smile.

"I am no Greek god," said Alex dryly. "And you will do better to consider what your God thinks about your behavior. Some things are right, and some things are wrong."

"Who is to say what is right or what is wrong. Some people say one thing and do another," she rationalized, noting her mother's hypocrisy. "I think I am entitled to a little pleasure in life. Is there anything wrong with that?"

"Wrong pleasures are wrong," said Alex with deep feeling, hoping he could discourage this girl who seemed so bent on destruction. "It's as simple as that." He watched her face to see some indication that his words were having a positive effect.

Salome looked him in the eye and said, "I came down here to have some fun, not to hear a lecture on morality. If you were a real man, you wouldn't waste our time resisting temptation. Don't you think I am temptation?" As she said this, she stood, raised her arms above her head, and turned slowly.

Alex shouted, "Get out!"

"Not so fast," said Salome. "Don't forget who I am and that I get what I want. You know what happened to Joseph when he refused Potiphar's wife."

"I'm afraid I don't know that story; but, whatever it is, it won't alter my decision," he said, turning his back on her again.

"Well," said Salome in a superior tone, "the moral of that story is that servants should do what they are told, or they could get into serious trouble."

"I know you can make trouble for me, but if trouble is to come, I would rather have it overtake me with a clean conscience."

Salome tossed her head. "I know of nothing so boring as a clean conscience." She was interrupted by her mother's voice outside, calling her name demandingly. "Salome! Where are you? Come out this instant!"

Salome whispered urgently to Alex, "Hide me! Don't let her find me here!"

"I will not hide you," said Alex. "Face your problems."

Instead of heeding this advice, Salome slapped herself hard across the face, tore her gown down from her shoulder, mussed her hair, and screamed, "Mother! Mother! Help me!" Then she ran to the door, threw it open, and fell to the floor.

Herodias ran to her and knelt by her side. "What has this beast been doing to you?" she cried. She helped Salome to her feet and said, "Go get the guards to take that man to the dungeon. He will be an old man before he sees the light of day again!" Then she quickly closed the door and stood guard in front of it while Salome ran for the guards.

Alex grabbed a few possessions and tied them in a cloth. He threw them out the narrow window and, with difficulty, squeezed through the opening which did not appear large enough to accommodate him. He dropped to the ground and ran into the night. When the cry was raised by the pursuing guards, he was a long way off.

16

"We leave this afternoon," Leah told Sarah. "Let's get things together. You will have to admit that this has been a pleasant visit for you." She said it with a knowing smile; she was glad to see the happiness that Sarah's contact with Alex had brought her. She felt like a mother to Sarah and shared her excitement.

"I would like to see Alex before we go," Sarah said. "Go ahead," said Leah, and then called after her, "Don't take all day; we have work to do."

Sarah went to the shop that Alex had shown her but was disappointed to find that he was not there. Although she was a tall, strong, capable young lady now, she still felt small and shy; and she did not really want to talk to the men who were there, his companions in labor. As she was leaving, one of them noticed her, so she plucked up her courage to approach them and asked timidly, "Where is Alex?"

"I wish I knew," said the man who had noticed her. "He did not come to work this morning, so we started without him. It was strange that he did not lay out the work for us, and he left no instructions. That is not like Alex."

"Perhaps he is sick in his room. I think I will check," said Sarah as she turned to go.

"You're wasting your time," said the man. "That's the first place we looked. He's not there and his bed has not been slept in. But his clothes are still there."

"What has happened to him?" asked Sarah, trying to hide her alarm.

"Your guess is as good as mine," shrugged the man. "I don't like the looks of this."

Sarah went to seek out Leah trying to suppress a growing fear in her breast. "Did he leave to avoid me?" she wondered aloud. "Was I pressing too hard? Did I say something that drove him off? Will he return tomorrow after I have left and resume his life as though I did not exist? At least he should have explained to me what he was about to do."

When Leah saw her coming, she knew something was wrong. With concern and kindness she asked, "Sarah, what is wrong?"

Sarah did not know how to start. Should she pour out her uncertainty? Should she simply relate the facts? She did neither; she began to cry. This made it difficult for Leah to get any information, but she understood it all when Sarah said, "He doesn't want me at all. He left to avoid me."

Leah put her arms around her, and this started a new flood of tears. "You don't know that, Sarah," she said gently. "There is probably a simple explanation for it all." Sarah snapped back, "Oh, is there? Then what is it?"

Leah, unoffended, said only, "Don't start assuming the worst. It is far better to assume the best, even if it does not work out that way. At least then you have a positive base from which to work. You are hurt and disappointed now, and I can understand that. But your reason is not real — not yet — and I hope you will find out that it was never real. You are carrying the burden of uncertainty, and that is a heavy burden, but don't make it heavier by adding fears of rejection. You will damage yourself and your opinion of Alex if you carry that."

"I know you are right," said Sarah, "but when Alex wasn't there, I saw all my hopes evaporate before my eyes."

"Do you know what I see before my eyes?" Leah diverted. "I see all this work to do before we leave, and that's a good thing for you, too. Work can be the best medicine for the heart. Let's get busy."

Herod Antipas stayed the night in his palace in Jerusalem, and early the next morning he left for his palace beyond Jordan. He was accompanied by his personal guards, fifty men in battle dress. Although the road from Jerusalem to Jericho was known for its thieves hiding in the waste places, the size of the contingent was more for show than for safety. Herod used every opportunity to show himself grand to the people of Judea.

He was not content with the portion of the kingdom that had been given to him; and, since talking with Herodias, he was even more discontent. She had fueled the greed, and he was willing to take the gamble.

He did not look forward to the task ahead of him. In his mind he tried to compose a speech that would make his position seem more reasonable; but, no matter how he phrased it, he appeared to be a cruel, heartless man, sending his wife away without reason. Oh, there were reasons — she had been indifferent to him, unwilling to help him with his grand plans; but he recognized that all of this had a hollow ring. The fact of the matter was that he had been captivated by the beauty of Herodias and overcome by her brazen approach. How different she was from Doris! How exciting! The Pharisees would have something to say, but he cared little for that. They needed him more than he needed them. Some of them were hypocrites anyhow!

He was beginning a new life, and he thought it would be best to make some changes. The palace would be dead no longer. It would be what it ought to be — the center of everything in the kingdom, but he would need more help. "I know what I will do," he said to himself, "I will bring some of my best people from Jerusalem when I return to get Herodias and Salome." What a good idea! What a life they would have!

He had planned to give his wife the "news" as soon as they reached the palace, but he lost his nerve. He was tired from the trip. He wanted to be prepared to handle her anger, but no matter what she said, no matter how much she cried, his mind was made up. She had to go!

When the confrontation came, Doris was angry — very angry. It was not that she wanted to stay with Herod; she held no love for him. The marriage had been her father's idea and he had hoped to profit from the match. She would certainly face his displeasure if she returned. But more than that was the shame of being rejected, sent home. She did not know how to handle this, since she was not a scheming woman and had no weapons in her arsenal. She was angry and she cried, but she went.

Herod lost no time in returning to Jerusalem to confront his brother Philip. Perhaps he would be more difficult to deal with than Doris had been. He hoped that Herodias would come to his aid.

The soldiers grumbled about another trip to Jerusalem, but this did not matter. Herod was as excited as a young man going to his wedding. He had no feeling for his wife's shame or his brother's pain; he put that completely out of his mind. His own happiness was all that mattered.

The confrontation with Philip was stormy but brief. Since the last visit, Philip had seen a change in Herodias and he knew that she was devising something. He had tried to talk with her, but she would say nothing. He had learned a long time before that he could not get Herodias to do anything she did not want to do. In fact, she made many decisions affecting him without even consulting him. Often he complained bitterly to himself, "One would think she was in charge here." Now she was at it again. After Herod had his say, Herodias took charge. She told Philip what she was going to do, daring him to try to stop her, challenging him to a battle of wills, which she would surely win. In the end, Philip simply gave up. He could not fight her.

Then he found himself experiencing a surprising feeling of relief. She was indeed ravishing, but she was also demanding and headstrong, determined to get her own way no matter what the cost. Such a woman was hard to live with. Antipas was a much stronger character than he was, that was true, but even he would have his troubles with her.

So Philip let her go. Ironically, when she started to remove some of the things she had decided to take with her, she took most of the furnishings. She would certainly feel at home in the new palace! With all that furniture, it would look like the old one!

Beyond the Jordan, the change of occupants at the palace did not go unnoticed. This choice piece of gossip spread on the wings of the wind. "It is a scandal, a shame to all of us," was the general consensus. The Pharisees talked about "a general breakdown of morals." Herod, no stranger to "diplomacy," answered by inviting them to his banquets and giving them seats of honor. Since they were such honored guests, they decided that it would be impolite to speak too harshly about their host and his morals.

There was a voice raised, however, a strong voice, an insistent voice, a voice in the wilderness, crying out for righteousness and justice. He was preaching near the Jordan River not far from the palace, and the echoes of his preaching shook the palace.

Sarah was now at that palace — she had come with Leah and the others Herod had brought from Jerusalem — and the events about to happen would shake her, profoundly shake her, so that she would never be the same again.

17

Alex fled into the night like a common criminal. It would have done him no good to try to defend himself against the false charge. Salome would tell her story, and that would be that. Most likely, he wouldn't get a chance to say a word. Would Salome feel some pangs of conscience and tell the truth? No chance! She had no conscience. All that she was concerned about was escaping her mother's wrath. No, she would not change her story; what happened to him meant nothing to her. If anything, she would be glad to see it happen; after all, she did threaten that bad things happen to servants who do not do what they are told. He had to run for it.

He heard the shouts of the guards, but he knew that they would not pursue him through the dark streets of Jerusalem; and, even if they did, he would have no trouble eluding them. But where could he go? He didn't dare try the house of friends because this could place them in danger. He needed a place that was secluded and offered at least a little shelter. He decided to spend the night on the Mount of Olives.

Wearily, brokenhearted, discouraged, he made his way out of the city and down into the valley of Kidron. Slowly he made his way up the other side, climbing the lower slopes of the Mount of Olives. During festivals, these slopes would be crowded with the poorer pilgrims who camped out in this area, but now they were deserted. He decided to climb higher, to a more secluded spot because he knew that, when daylight came, this would be a busy place. On the Mount of Olives were two large cedar trees, and under these were shops that sold the things needed for the Temple worship — doves, lambs, oil, meal. He passed these and went higher, until he found a place under the ancient, gnarled olive trees. Here he lay down to sleep.

But sleep would not come. He was uncomfortable, but, more than that, he was distressed. "How unfair life is at times," he fretted aloud. "Look what Salome has done to me. I have never done anything to her; I never even spoke to her before tonight. But that selfish, deceitful, evil hussy has ruined my life, and she gets off completely free! Now, look at my life; all I have worked for these years is gone in a moment because of that liar. My position and work are gone, my chance of advancement is gone, even my place to live is gone.''

Then he thought of Sarah and felt the keenest loss of all. Just when he had found her again! What would she think? How could he let her know what had happened? He had to do something about that. He decided that the best thing to do was to wait until after dark the next evening and go to the palace and see what could be done. It was too dangerous to try during the daylight hours.

Perhaps he was right. Herodias was very angry when she found that he had escaped. She hurried to Philip and ordered him to do something about it. Philip listened to her story but was reluctant to act because he did not believe that things had happened the way she described. "Tell me again," he stalled. "How did you find her?"

Herodias narrowed her dark eyes at him. "She wasn't in her room, and I was afraid that she was up to some mischief, so I went looking for her."

Philip thought skeptically, *Yes, she probably was up to some mischief,* but he asked, "Did you hear her calling for help?"

"Well . . . no."

"Why did you go looking in the servants' quarters? Did you expect to find her there?"

Herodias knew what Philip was driving at. He did not think Salome had been taken by force; he thought she had been there by choice.

"Don't you believe your own daughter?" she demanded with vehemence, knowing that neither of them did. Then came the real issue. "But he ridiculed me!" she shouted. Her eyes were flashing again, "He made a fool out of me! There I was, guarding the door to an empty room. When the guards arrived, I pushed it open and said, 'Arrest that man!' The room was empty! I felt like a fool! I'm going to make him pay for that; nobody's going to make a fool out of me!" Seeing that she was not going to get any help from Philip, she stormed out of the room. She thought of confronting Salome to find out the truth — Philip's questions had raised her doubts, too — but that didn't matter now. This was a matter between herself and the man who had defied her. He would learn!

Morning came, and Alex stirred his aching bones; he was not used to sleeping on the ground nor in the chilly open air. He checked to see that his possessions were still there. All he owned in the world, wrapped in one cloth. He had grabbed his money — he was beginning to accumulate a good sum — his engraving tools, and some of his finest pieces. He was not destitute, but he couldn't live on this forever. He would have to make some big decisions. Soon! But first, Sarah.

He was hungry, so the first order of business would have to be breakfast. Then, he would buy a warmer coat in case he had to spend another night on the ground. Even if Philip's guards were looking for him, he felt he would be reasonably safe if he kept in the crowds of the marketplace.

The market was crowded and pleasantly noisy; it was the beating heart of the city, alive with activity. Farmers from the outlying areas were arriving with produce to feed the thriving city, and a long camel caravan was arriving from some distant place. He could not count all the camels, but he had heard that, at times, the caravans numbered two hundred animals.

The marketplace was divided into bazaars according to the merchandise being sold: fruits and vegetables in one area, livestock and chickens in another, cloth and clothing in another. Of course, everything to be sold had to pass by the tax collector whose lucrative district covered the marketplace. There he sat at his table with his money-box. The man was a Jew and had paid a good price for this position; but, with the rates he charged, he had gotten his money back many times over.

In the bazaars, activity was brisk. Nothing was sold for a set price, but even the smallest item required some bargaining. Once the deal was struck, however, the weights and measures had to be exact, the law required that; and there were police who supervised the trading to make sure that things were done properly.

The streets were crowded with buyers, sellers, camels, donkeys, and every now and then, a wagon. Since most of the roads were quite poor, there were not many of these, but some of the thousand wagons Herod used in the building of the Temple had survived. Although they could carry a great deal, actually they were at a disadvantage in the narrow, winding streets.

In a little while, Alex lost his apprehension and began to enjoy the fine day. There was nothing he could do until nightfall. He had a good breakfast and then bought another coat. He walked idly up and down the streets, looking in the shops, always on the lookout for guards.

He turned a corner and, to his surprise, found himself in the slave market. He had not visited that part of the city since he had stood there with Sarah. He recognized the awning under which they had stood. He crossed the street to pause under it. How long ago that seemed! Now that he thought of it, even then he had known that Sarah was something special.

Once more, he was not sure that he would ever even see her again. He remembered how his being a Gentile stood like a high wall between them. How much he had changed! When Sarah had asked him to help her pray, he realized that his gods had no effect on his life; Sarah, on the other hand, found strength and courage from her God. If only he could talk to her about these things! Perhaps they would get a chance someday; the wall did not seem so high anymore.

The day seemed so long; he was not used to having nothing to do, and he didn't like it. It was barely dark when he made his way to the rear gate of Philip's palace to see what he could find out about Sarah. He hoped that one of his friends would come out for some reason and would be willing to convey the message to her that he was outside and wanted to talk to her. Things did not work out that way. After a long, long wait, a gardener came out on his way home. Alex did not know him by name and did not know whether he would raise the alarm and turn him in, but he had to take the chance.

To his relief, the man was not surprised to see him and had no intention of helping Philip or Herodias with anything. But the news the man gave him was disheartening. "They all left this morning," he said. "I think they were going to the Maccabean palace."

It was late; Alex would have to wait until the next day to check this out. This meant another night on the Mount of Olives. It was a good thing he had bought another coat.

He had intended to wait until dark the next day to go to the palace, but by late afternoon, he could wait no longer. He was taking a chance. "But after all," he reasoned, "this is not Philip's palace, and I should be safe here." He waited around the corner from the palace where he could watch the rear gate and soon was rewarded. A man — he looked like a tradesman — came out of the gate and came his way. Alex pretended that he had business in the palace and needed to know the best time to get in. He asked a number of questions, and in the conversation he learned what had happened; most of the people had left in a procession that morning. "Where are they going?" The man didn't know; he thought they took the Jericho road.

Alex made his way back to the Mount of Olives with a heavy heart. Something told him he had lost her again. What would he do now? Where would he go? He said to himself, "This requires a complete reevaluation of my life. I have the feeling that the decisions I make now will determine all of my future happiness. I must examine my options carefully."

One by one, he thought of the paths open to him. He could go back to his homeland, Greece. But why? What was there for him? He had been gone so long that he did not feel he belonged there. He crossed off that option. He did not think it would be safe to stay in Jerusalem; but, if he wanted to be successful in his trade, he had to locate in an important city. Damascus? Perhaps he could find Benazra and get some help from him. No . . . too

far to go on such a slim hope. Caesarea? Possibly. It might be a good place
to do business. But wait! What about Jericho? Suddenly, that seemed the
obvious choice. Wherever Sarah was, she was no doubt closer to Jericho
than to Caesarea. It would be a good place for his trade. All the pilgrims going east from Jerusalem would pass through there. That felt right. It was
Jericho. He would start the next morning.

The afternoon sun was low as he made his way up the Mount of Olives.
The road took a sudden turn and the Temple was clearly in view below him;
the golden spikes on the roof were ablaze with the setting sun. The vast,
massive Temple walls, built with stones twenty-four feet long, were im-
pressive from here. The marble of the Temple was snow-white; the marble
of the walls was variegated, like the waves of the sea. The original plan had
called for covering the walls with gold, but they were so beautiful the way
they were that the decision was made to leave them.

Alex stood for a long time taking in the sight. It evoked memories of a
time in his past when he was just a lad. His father had taken him to Ephesus
to the temple of Artemis — the Romans called her Diana. That temple had
taken more than two centuries to build, and it was considered one of the
''Seven Wonders of the World.'' It was there he had seen some of the
world's greatest silversmiths at work, and he had decided to be like them.
Artemis was supposed to be the daughter of Zeus, the twin sister of Apollo.
She was pictured as a beautiful young lady, a huntress and protector of wild
creatures. This was beautiful, but the worship in her temple was not; it was
a continual orgy.

Two temples, Alex thought. *Two religions. Which is for me?* As a matter
of fact, Diana meant nothing to him. He knew that the void in his heart
could not be filled by a silver statue he made by his own hands. He felt
strongly that the Temple now in view should be his temple.

If only I knew the way to this God! he said to himself as he left the scene
behind. With this thought still on his mind, he found a place under an old
olive tree and lay down to sleep.

The next morning the sun was already up before Alex awoke. He felt
comfortable and refreshed, perhaps because he was getting used to sleeping
on the ground, perhaps because of his frame of mind. Although his difficulties remained, he had a plan of action and he would be on the move as
soon as he had breakfast. What awaited him in Jericho, he didn't know, but
the decision seemed right. The warm sun and the beautiful day made him
feel optimistic. His optimism did not make him foolhardy, however, and he
always tried to hide himself in a group just in case the guards were still
searching for him. When he left Jerusalem, he waited near the gate until

a good-sized crowd came along, evidently on the way to Jericho, and he slipped away among them.

He felt a twinge of sadness as he left. His stay in Jerusalem had been a strange mixture of good things and bad. It was the city itself that held an attraction for him that he could not explain. He did not know where the road of his life would lead, but he hoped he would see the city again, next time, under more pleasant circumstances!

Alex arrived in Jericho just after midday. The fragrance of the balsam trees was in the air, and the breezes were warm, and the prospect of sleeping on the ground here did not seem to be unpleasant at all. He did not even need the extra coat he had purchased in Jerusalem.

He took some time to look over the city and then went to the market to get some bread and fish at a shop that sold food to the travelers. The proprietor of the shop seemed friendly, so Alex asked him, "I have just arrived from Jerusalem; how would I go about finding work?"

"You must be led by the hand of God!" replied the shopkeeper. "Not an hour ago the owner of a balsam plantation was here looking for workers. I think he would be happy to have you." Then the shopkeeper gave directions, and Alex started off.

As he walked along, he thought, *The man said, "You must be led by the hand of God." I wonder if that is true. Does God care about me? Can it be that I am walking this road, at this time, because God has plans for me? I don't know! But the only way to find out is to keep walking to see where this road leads.*

The road led to the plantation and a man named James, a disciple of John the Baptist.

"Do you have some work for me?" Alex asked hopefully.

James looked him over and saw that he was tall and lean. Although his hands were long and slender, he was obviously capable of hard work. A brief interview convinced James that he was a trustworthy man. "Yes," said James, "I have a place for you, and I will pay you a penny a day."

"Could I sleep under your trees at night? I have no place to stay," said Alex.

"I can do better than that," said James. "There is a shelter in the middle of the grove; I think you will find that to be very comfortable."

"Could I start to work now?" Alex asked. "I am not used to being idle."

"If you do," replied James, "I will pay you a penny for this day."

Alex was surprised and pleased by this show of generosity. It would be a joy to work for a man with this kind of spirit. He would give him more than his money's worth.

Some time later when James came to pay Alex, he said, "I am a disciple of John the Baptist, a true man of God. Tomorrow my wife, Ruth, and I will be going to hear him. He is preaching in the wilderness near the river, teaching about the Kingdom of God, and we would like you to go with us. Alex did not hesitate. "I would like that," he said. "I have been looking for someone who can show me the ways of your God."

"Then tomorrow will be a great day for you; John can certainly do that!" replied James.

The next day as they walked along, they talked about many things. Alex liked Ruth immediately. She was a cheerful woman, and from their first greeting, she made Alex feel like an old friend. She seemed genuinely concerned about him; and, before he knew it, Alex was opening up some of the recent chapters of his life. In the course of the conversation, he told them about Sarah and her great faith in God, about her hopes for Israel, how he had lost her, and how he hoped to find her again. Also, he mentioned that he was a silversmith and had been in charge of the business at Philip's palace.

"A silversmith?" said James. "Then you shouldn't be working in the groves. If you have a talent like that, there is a better place for you, and I know where it is."

The silversmith in town, it came out, was a friend of James'. He was getting old and his hands were getting unsteady. He was looking for someone good enough to take over.

Can this be happening to me? thought Alex. *Is this the way the Lord leads?*

No wonder his heart was open to the preaching of John! No wonder he was eager to respond when he was given the opportunity!

18

His name was John and he was raised in the hills of Hebron. He had been born to elderly parents and was in the priestly line, but the life of a priest did not appeal to him. The solitude of the wilderness was more to his liking. Often on a stormy night when the heavens would open up and pour out torrents of rain, he would stand in the open, unprotected, with the rain beating on his upturned face and beard, hands raised to heaven, and his strong voice, overcoming the noise of the raging storm, praising God who was above it all.

From the beginning, his parents had told him that his birth and his calling were special. He did not need to be told; he felt this deep inside, like the glow in a furnace. He was sure the day of judgment was at hand and the warning had to be sounded. He had considered going to Jerusalem to proclaim his message in the Temple court, but he had decided against that. He was out of his element in Jerusalem; he could not survive being cooped up and shut in by the walls — the wild wilderness was his home.

When he could keep silent no longer, he went to a place on the Jordan River near Jericho where the main road led to Jerusalem. For a long time he stood and evaluated the location. This was where Joshua and the people of Israel had crossed into the land to begin a new life. Perhaps he, too, should cross and preach on the other side. No! not on the other side! Israel was not on the victory side, but on the wilderness side. The River Jordan would show the crossing to the right side, the side of victory and obedience to God, to truly become His people. And the sign would be baptism in the river! Yes, that was it!

This was the place. To the north, he could see Mount Nebo; Moses had climbed that mountain to view the land of promise, to see the vision of the future, a golden future for the people of God. He could see that too, however dimly. Not far away was the brook Cherith where Elijah had waited during the dry days when God had shut up the heavens. The heavens were certainly shut up to Israel now; and soon, he hoped, he could bring news of an abundance of rain.

Yes, this was the place!

Herodias had made herself at home in her new palace. From the day she arrived, everyone knew who was in charge. Previously, Herod Antipas gave the orders; his wife said little. At times, she made suggestions to the servants — suggestions, but not orders. Now a strong, demanding woman was in charge. On top of that, the new contingent of servants brought from Jerusalem added to the problem. Understandably, there was friction between the new and the old; and, since the old servants represented a challenge to the authority of Herodias, she installed the new ones in positions of authority and responsibility. She chose Leah to fill one of the responsible positions.

Life was not dull; every evening there was some kind of dinner or banquet. Any trivial excuse was turned into a reason for a celebration. The palace became the hub of all activity, and anything that happened that had any significance was a subject of discussion and debate in the banquet hall. The man who preached by the river soon became the main topic of conversation.

Herodias was presiding at one of her banquets, daintily plucking at some of the exotic food on her silver plate when she overheard one of the Pharisees at a table near her. He was talking about this strange man, and Herodias interrupted her own conversation to hear what he had to say. She heard only a snatch of the conversation, but what she heard fascinated her. He was saying, "He is the most powerful man I have ever heard."

Herodias said to herself, "I will have to see this man! I like men, and I admire power; I will have to see this combination for myself. I never heard that Pharisee express admiration for anyone like that before; he would never praise the man without good reason. This is something I must investigate."

To her surprise, Sarah was summoned to Herodias's chamber. What could this woman possibly want from her? If she had some complaint about her work, she would have had Leah speak to her. Was this good news or bad news? Sarah came to the door of the chamber and paused; she did not look forward to this meeting. Then she knocked timidly and a pleasant voice called, "Come in." Sarah opened the door and, stepping just inside, stood politely as a servant should, waiting for Herodias to speak. The woman smiled a gracious, friendly smile, and with a sweeping gesture of her hand — a hand covered with expensive rings — she said sweetly, "Sarah, come, sit down. I need you to help me with a little plan of mine. I think you will enjoy it as much as I will."

Sarah did not know what to say; she had not expected such a friendly encounter. Herodias was making it seem as though they were just two girls conspiring together on some harmless prank. But she was still on guard and decided that if she said nothing, she would not commit herself to anything. But Herodias was going to get a commitment before she proceeded, so she said in her most winsome voice, "This must be between just the two of us. No one else must know. I have to have your promise on this."

She waited for Sarah to promise. What could she do? Sarah was in no position to question her first, and she could not refuse before she heard what it was all about; that would be unthinkable. Herodias had her trapped. Sarah knew it; Herodias knew it. So Sarah said weakly, "You have my promise."

"Good," said Herodias. "You will enjoy this."

At this point Sarah was sure she would not enjoy whatever it was that she was being forced into, but she was anxious to find out what it was. "You have heard of this John fellow — you know, the one preaching by the river? Well, we are going to hear him, and no one will know about it. I want you to get me some old clothes — you know, servants's clothes — like the ones that you are wearing, and get some food for us to take along, and when a group of people come along on the way to hear him, we will just join them, and no one will know who we are. Are you willing?"

Sarah had already given her promise, but even if she hadn't she would have now. She wanted to hear John even more than Herodias did. From the reports she had heard, this man was saying what she felt deep in her soul. Perhaps he was even the deliverer she had hoped to be. Yes, she would gladly go to hear him; she would welcome the chance.

"Now remember," said Herodias, "tell no one. This is our little secret. We go tomorrow morning."

When Sarah met Herodias the next morning, she hardly recognized her. Gone were all the rings and jewelry, her face was scrubbed clean, and her hair tucked discretely under a shawl. As they passed through the gate, Sarah spoke to the guards, but they did not appear to recognize her companion. This pleased Herodias very much, and she told Sarah, "We will have to do this more often; it's fun going around like an ordinary person."

Sarah thought of several clever replies to her condescension, but decided that they would not be wise; but she did have to admit that it bothered her when Herodias spoke in such a condescending tone about "ordinary people."

The crowd at the riverside was enormous; several were heard to exclaim in wonder, "It looks like all Jerusalem is here!" Indeed, it was a surprising sight to see so many people gathered in such a desolate place to listen to a man who had no credentials, no official standing, and would most likely say some hard things that would make them feel uncomfortable. But there they were; the rich and the poor, city dwellers and country people, priests and publicans, Pharisees and soldiers. Such a thing had never been seen before.

There was a stir at the far edge of the crowd. The man, John, was approaching with his disciples. Without haste, he eased his way through the crowd, but he spoke to no one. He didn't even return their greetings. It was as though he was oblivious to their presence. He made his way to a mound in the center of the crowd and stood upon it. It was then that Sarah got a good look at him.

He was a large man — at least he seemed large, standing as he did high above the crowd. He wore a rough garment of camel hair with a wide belt around his waist. His hair was full, coal black, as was his ample beard. His eyes were riveting, but it was his voice that captured attention. It was deep and resonant and seemed to come from the center of his being. It rumbled like thunder and echoed and reechoed across the wilderness plain. As soon as he began to speak, a hush fell over the crowd.

Perhaps he said the same thing day after day with additions or changes. His message struck a responsive chord, and the audience hung on to every word. It was evident that if he called for a response, he would get one.

Herodias turned to Sarah and said, "Now there's a man! What power! What magnetism! I think he is strong enough to tame any woman — even me!" She began watching the reaction to John as much as the preacher himself.

Sarah was startled and disappointed. She was stirred by the powerful message from God; Herodias was feeling stirrings of a different kind. The message was wasted on her.

Sarah turned her attention to John again. He was saying, "The Shechinah glory has departed from Israel. There is no king in Jerusalem; and a foreigner, a Roman, and not even a noble Roman, but a Roman knight, Pontius Pilate, rules us and oppresses from his throne in Caesarea."

The mention of the name *Caesarea* brought back a flood of memories to Sarah, especially, her first sight of the Roman legions.

"God will set His king upon the Holy Hill of Zion," continued John, "but He will not do this as long as the land is full of wickedness and violence. God calls you, God commands you to come down into the waters of baptism, into the waters of repentance, and have your sins washed away."

When he was finished, there was a large response. People were loudly confessing their sins. A man in fine robes was one of the loudest. "I know him," scoffed Herodias. "He is a leading publican, a cheat and a thief; it will take more than the River Jordan to make an honest man of him."

But when John made his way into the river, the publican was first in line; and the line grew. Some came up out of the water shouting and praising God, and the line grew longer.

Then Sarah recognized someone in line. It was Alex! She almost cried out in delight, and turned to point him out to Herodias. She knew nothing of the events that had sent him on the run and had no idea that Herodias had commanded that he be thrown into prison. Fortunately, when she turned to talk to Herodias, she found that she had started to walk away, so Sarah said nothing and followed.

"What a man!" said Herodias. "Did you see how he controlled that crowd? What a leader he would make if he had someone like me to guide him! We must have him at the palace for one of our banquets. What a performance he could give!"

A few weeks later he "gave the performance." Some of his disciples advised him not to go, and Herod's people tried to apply subtle pressure. John stood in the middle and made his own decision. He had a message to deliver, and he would make use of any opportunity that came along. He agreed to go.

The banquet was most elaborate. John declined the place of honor; he would not even recline at one of the tables in the rear. Instead, he sat in lonely isolation on the floor in the corner. This did not displease the host or his guests; they regarded him as a queer character and considered this part of their show. They were here to see him perform, as they would watch any other attraction that Herod provided at his banquets. John ate nothing that was provided for him. In all his life he had never been tainted by the danties that filled the tables around him. Seeing this, Leah said to Sarah, "Go ask him if he would like some bread or meat or something to drink."

Sarah was glad for the opportunity to have some contact with this man of God. Very politely she approached him and relayed Leah's question. His response did not surprise her, "I will neither eat bread nor drink water in this den of iniquity. I am here to issue a warning from Almighty God, but I will not be contaminated by their extravagance."

Sarah turned to leave; she took a step or two, but something within her caused her to turn back. Quickly, quietly she murmured, "I, too, sigh and cry for the deliverance of Israel and for the reign of righteousness." Without saying more, she turned and walked away.

Although the main attraction that night was this man from the wilderness, it seemed as though every banquet had to have its preliminary entertainment — dancing girls, comedians, jugglers. Sarah wondered if John would cry out against these things and cause a scene, but he did not. He sat impassively and looked at the floor. He was not here to complain about outward signs, but inner corruption. His time would come, and he would make good use of it.

Finally, Herod had some glowing words about John, half in earnest, half in jest. John was not now surrounded by eager listeners, but rather by critics and detractors; not by a fervent congregation, but by people looking for entertainment and diversion after a long banquet. They were not eager to hear, but eager to gawk.

This whole affair had been arranged by Herodias, and she was pleased with herself for planning such an interesting evening. She also had this man, whom she had only seen from a distance, right here in her home territory. And she was not now dressed in servants' clothes! She had spent the afternoon preparing herself in her finest clothing and jewelry, and as she evaluated herself in her mirror, she determined that she was beautiful enough to melt even a man of stone, to stir longing, even in the heart of this man from the wilderness. If he did not pay proper attention to her, she would use her position of authority to do something about it. She was a determined woman, and certainly this uncultured man was no match for her. She watched him intently as he rose to speak.

He began quietly: "I stand in a palace fit for a king, but I do not belong in a palace. My home is the wilderness with the sky and the stars for my roof and the earth for my bed. I am here surrounded by people clothed in rich garments and jewels; my only garment is the one you see upon me now, rough and crude. I stand now among people with position and honor; the only honor, the only position I have is given by God, and if God has not given it, I have none."

The people were listening. Sarah stood just outside an open door, her heart beating rapidly. What had these people expected from him? Had they expected that he would rant and rave, wave his arms and shout? What had they expected? Certainly they did not expect this man who spoke in such measured tones. But even his quiet tones were overlaid with authority. He was not the entertainment — he was in charge.

"Who am I? 'You must be Elijah,' they say to me. 'Aren't you Elijah?' I answer them, 'No, I am not Elijah.' Some are even bolder, 'You are the Messiah, aren't you?' I answer them, 'No I am not the Messiah.' 'Who are you?' they call, and you may very well be asking that, too; and I will give you the answer. I am a voice, like a voice crying in the wilderness; just a voice! Who I am is not important; the message that I bear is important. Here is God's message: Prepare the way for the Lord; the Messiah is on His way. If you will repent of your sin and wickedness, you will be God's children. If not, the ax will chop away at the roots of the tree, and the branches will be burned with fire. God's judgment is at the door."

Now they felt uneasy. He spoke with such authority that it seemed impossible to challenge his statements. He sounded like an Old Testament prophet.

Then he turned to the religious leaders who were there and spoke of things that everyone knew were true and that should not be; some of them burned with shame and some burned with anger. The Pharisees present had been enjoying John's criticism of the priests, but then he turned to them. He was harsher with them than he had been with the priests, and, they complained, he made them all to appear to be hypocrites. They were not pleased.

Finally, he turned and faced Herod and Herodias. The room was still. Surely he would not speak against them! Surely, as an invited guest, he would be very careful of what he said! Surely, he would recognize that this man held the power of life or death over him! Surely, he would just speak in general terms and be finished!

But John did not come for this; he did not come to entertain, but he came to lay the ax at the root of the tree. He looked at Herod intently, and it seemed as if his eyes were piercing into Herod's very soul. When he looked at Herodias, the smile was gone from her face; her eyes blazed and met his in challenge, defying him, and she thought, *Wilderness man, you better watch your words! You be careful what you say to me!*

"And you, Herod," John began, "your sin was not hidden in a corner. I know of it; all Israel knows of it; and God in Heaven knows of it! And you do not care! Openly, under the guise of friendship, you enter your brother's house and take away his wife. Where is your true wife? Sent away in shame. Is she guilty of sin? Has she been unfaithful? Has she committed some great evil? No! She has been sent away because you wanted the woman who is beside you now, the woman who shares your adultery; the woman who has become nothing more than a harlot."

The words were scarcely out of his mouth when Herodias leaped to her feet and yelled, "Throw him out! Throw that man out! If I ever see him again, I will kill him with my bare hands!"

The place was in an uproar. John did not wait for any farewells. With long strides he made his way out of the hall, out of the palace, down the road to the wilderness. The night was dark, and the stars were bright. He gulped the cool night air as though he were trying to rid his lungs of the pollution of the palace. He did not even consider what the repercussions from the evening would be. That was up to God.

19

Back in the palace, the banquet ended abruptly. The guests had come for a performance, and they had gotten more than they had bargained for. Herodias wondered how she ever could have admired this man and lamented the fact that she had been the one to invite him to do this despicable thing. She had imagined herself infatuated with this powerful man; now that he had assaulted her pride, the remembrance fueled the roaring fires of bitter hatred.

With bitterness and anger she hissed at Herod, "I want to see that man dead! If you are a man at all, you will make him pay dearly for his insolence here tonight. Torture him! Throw him to the wild beasts in the arena! Tie him to a post, and I will beat him to death myself!"

Herod said nothing; he had seen her angry before, but not like this. She frightened him; she might easily turn this anger on him. He would stay out of her way until her anger cooled down.

By morning it had cooled down; it was no longer a volcano, but it was still a burning furnace. With steely anger she said, "I demand that you send the soldiers to capture that man and put him to death! I demand it!"

Soothingly, Herod said, "I understand how you feel, but you must remember that the people regard him as a prophet; and, if we act unwisely, we will have a rebellion on our hands."

Herodias sneered at him. "If you let him continue at the river, the people will make him their leader, their king, and you will be through. All he needs to say to the crowd is, 'Go clean out that den of evil,' and they will come like a tidal wave and overwhelm us all. Even Rome could not save you then."

Herod turned away; he did not like being told what to do, but Herodias was right. John was in his territory, and he was responsible. It would be a wise move, a prudent move. So he called his captain and gave the orders.

When Sarah learned that John was in the palace dungeon, she immediately wanted to call down the wrath of God on Herod and Herodias because of this unspeakably evil deed. Eternally practical, Leah said simply, "You may well do that, but right now you have a more gentle task to perform. Here, take this bread and water to John. Carry this lantern with you, it's dark down there."

110

"I'm going to find a way to set him free," said Sarah. "God will give me the strength to deliver this good man. I will find a way."

"That you will never do!" said Leah bluntly. "You will find him chained to the wall in the dungeon which is little more than a pit with an iron gate for a door. The guards know that they will forfeit their lives if he escapes. No, forget that, Sarah. You are never going to get him out."

"Will I get into trouble if I talk to him?"

"No, I don't think so. The guards have been given orders to let his disciples in to talk with him; but they never open the iron gate or remove the chains. Now that it is night and your work is done, you may talk as long as you like."

Sarah had never seen the dungeon before. She went down many steps and was sure that she was far underground. There were no windows, and everything smelled of musty earth. Two guards sat under a lamp playing some kind of game with pieces of bone. They pointed to the long, low tunnel and said, "You will find him down there."

Sarah's small lamp did not cast very much light, so she walked carefully over the uneven stones. The damp tunnel came to an abrupt end, and Sarah almost bumped into the iron gate. She lifted her lamp high, and it cast a circle of flickering light over the dungeon floor. What she saw, broke her heart. John was chained to the wall by chains attached to each leg. He could reach the food Sarah offered only by getting down on his hands and knees and reaching forward.

Sarah said to him, "I am the one who talked to you at the banquet; do you remember? My name is Sarah. I'm the one who offered you food. It's awful for you to be here! I will find some way to get you out of this prison."

John replied blandly, "Only the hand of God and the will of God can release me from this place. If it is not God's will, you will struggle in vain. But," he softened, "one thing you can do . . . you can join me in a prayer of thanksgiving for this food." John raised his strong voice in joyful praise and then sang a Psalm. Sarah felt the joy of the presence of the Lord there, and her tiny lamp seemed to cast a holy glow around them. The dank prison had been transformed into a Temple.

Sarah did not sleep well that night; she could not get her mind off John in such atrocious circumstances. She felt a keen sense of disappointment because, after seeing the dungeon, she realized that nothing she could do would make it possible for her to free him. It would take God's miracle.

But the miracle did not come. The weeks dragged by, and the months. Herodias kept pressing Herod to do away with him, but Herod was afraid to. He feared the reaction from the people; but, more than that, he knew that John was a true man of God, and the power of God was evident in his life. He feared the wrath of God if he killed him. The Pharisees around him proclaimed John an enemy of the state and warned Herod not to let him go. Mighty Herod found himself trapped, so he did nothing.

Each night Sarah brought John bread and water and stayed to talk. It wasn't long before she was telling him about her life, especially about her thoughts of being a deliverer like Esther. She was embarrassed as she told this; it seemed so foolish to say such things to such a wise and valiant man. What would he think of her?

John's dark beard smiled at her. "I know exactly what you feel! I have felt the same thing. More than that, I have known that God's hand has been upon me from the beginning. I have always known I had a special ministry; and, at times, I thought I would be the deliverer. Now I know better. I am not the deliverer, but the forerunner, the herald who runs ahead and shouts, 'Prepare the way of the Lord.' This is what I am called to do."

"Then the Messiah is coming soon?" asked Sarah with intense interest.

"He is already here," said John. "I baptized Him in the river, and the heavens opened, and a dove lighted upon Him, and I heard a voice, God's voice, saying, 'This is My Son.' " John's eyes softened and he became silent. He was reliving the whole event in his mind; he was transported into that scene. In the glow of the small lamp, Sarah could see his face change and it seemed to shine with the glory of God.

As the days passed, Sarah became worried about John's health. "How long can a man go chained to a wall, never seeing the sun, never feeling a breeze, or breathing real air, never seeing a tree or a flower?" Then she wept. She determined that for John's sake she would never let him see her that way; but, the next night when she saw him, her resolve disappeared and her tears flowed like a river. At first, John thought she was in some kind of trouble, but then she told how sad she was for him.

For an instant, she thought he was going to weep, but he steeled himself and said, "I am ashamed to say this, but I have become very discouraged. Can you believe that? Me, John the Baptist! I have doubts about everything. I thought surely the Messiah would deliver me out of this prison" — he raised his chained foot — "but that has not happened. I know I have been called to a great ministry, but how can I minister when I am chained to a wall in a hole in the earth? I thought the Messiah would begin to establish the Kingdom, but nothing has happened yet. In the darkness of this dungeon, I have even doubted the voice of God I heard at the river. The sky does not open upon me anymore. I have sent my disciples to talk to the Messiah for me."

Sarah said wisely, "It is the darkness and isolation that is doing this to you. If you could stride across the wilderness with the sun in your face and the wind in your hair, if you could preach again by the river, if you could see people repenting and asking to be baptized, your doubts would disappear like morning dew before the summer sun."

"I hope you are right, Sarah," said John, "and I thank you."

Herodias was becoming impatient. Her anger had turned to cold determination that ate away at her like an evil disease. It tormented her, it became an obsession. She knew now that Herod would do nothing, or if he acted at all, it would be to let John go. It was up to her; she would finish this business.

Herod's birthday was approaching, and this was always an excuse for a great celebration. Herodias decided she would use the occasion to accomplish her purpose. She planned the most elaborate banquet ever held in the palace. The hall was transformed into a desert oasis with Arab tents, palm trees, pools, and sand dunes. Guests were asked to come dressed in Arab garb, and the musicians were especially chosen for the occasion.

All of this was secondary, though. The main part of her plan involved her daughter, Salome. She would need her complete cooperation, and she had to make sure that she followed orders exactly. She could not let Salome know what she was planning; she might not be able to handle it, and it might upset her performance. She would have to manipulate her carefully.

The day before the banquet, she called Salome to her room and said, "And now for the big surprise! Salome, you are to be the star performer at the banquet."

Salome responded in surprise, "Me? What am I supposed to do?"

Herodias spoke in a very intimate voice, as though they were coconspirators, "You are to play the part of an Arab slave dancing girl. When the music begins, you will emerge from the tent and begin your dance."

Salome considered this for a moment and then asked her mother, "There's more to this than just the dance, isn't there? Why have you waited until now to tell me? Why don't you have someone else do the dance?"

Herodias would not get her cooperation without telling her something, but how much? She let out a long breath and sagged in her chair, as though Salome was forcing her to confide all. This was not going to be so easy. She had come this far; she would not turn back.

"Salome, I need your help. You know how stubborn Herod can be. I have been trying to get him to do something important for me but he has refused. He becomes as stubborn as a mule. If you will help me, I think I can break down his resistance."

Now Salome was even more suspicious. "What is it you want from him?"

"It's a secret — I will tell you at the banquet, but I will tell you now that it is something big." She added pragmatically, "If you help, I'll do something big for you when this is over. Will you help me?"

"You just want me to do a dance?" asked Salome. "There must be more to it than that?"

"Just a dance, but a very special dance. You know how some of those slave girls dance! I want you to outdo them. I want you to be so suggestive that you could move a stone statue, and as you dance, throw off your clothes, one piece at a time."

Salome looked at her mother in astonishment. "Mother!" she said, "I couldn't do that!"

"Of course you can! I saw the dance you were doing for the servants back at the other palace. You knew what you were doing! You knew every eye was glued on you! And I know how Herod looks at you! I want you to work him up into such a state that he will give us anything we want."

Herodias stood up; the discussion was over. All Salome could say was, "Mother!"

Herodias made sure that every aspect of the banquet was exactly as she wanted. She ordered a special wine, a strong wine, and gave orders that it should be served only to Herod. She left nothing to chance. During the banquet, she said to Herod, "I have a very special present for your birthday, something I am sure you will like." This intrigued Herod, and he coaxed and coaxed her to tell him what it was. She smiled beguilingly, told him to wait, and filled his wine glass again. She did not drink; she was so nervous already that she could not eat.

At last the time came for the finale. Most of the lamps were extinguished, leaving a circle of light in front of Herod. The music began with a slow, insistent beat, and Salome emerged from the tent and moved into the center of the circle. Herod gasped when he saw her and realized what was about to happen. His face was already flushed from the wine; he never took his eyes off her as she moved to the beat of the music. Herodias had carefully instructed the musicians, and they knew exactly what to do. Salome knew also.

Sarah entered the hall with a serving tray and stopped in her tracks when she saw what was happening. All of a sudden, she was transported back to the time she sat with Alex and Salome danced in the back courtyard. A wave of emptiness swept over her; she had tried to put Alex out of her mind, supposing that he had deserted her, but now her loneliness was revived. She remembered how Alex had turned his back and rejected the sensuous performance. She decided that she would do the same, so she turned and left.

It was a good thing she did; if she had stayed and witnessed the events that followed, she would have had memories that would have haunted her for the rest of her life, memories that would have caused her to awake in the night screaming.

Salome danced as her mother had instructed; Herod reacted as Herodias knew he would. However, even she could never have anticipated the loud declaration he made for all to hear. In a roaring voice he said, "Salome, ask me for anything you want — anything at all — up to half of my kingdom, and I swear, I will give it to you!"

Salome whispered to her mother, "What shall I ask?"

All that had been seething inside of Herodias gushed forth as she said, "The head of John the Baptist on a platter — here! — now!"

Herod's flushed face blanched. He knew that John was a prophet, but he had given his oath before all of the guests; he was afraid to back down. *It's not my fault,* he said to his guilty heart. *The blame lies with Herodias. I have no choice!*

He gave the order.

20

In the kitchen they were making preparations to conclude the banquet and begin the job of cleaning up. The music had stopped in the banquet hall, and Leah assumed that the final speeches were being made. Then they heard loud sounds of confusion: women screaming, voices raised, someone shouting. A servant girl burst through the kitchen door, crying hysterically. "Don't go in there! Don't go in there!" she cried over and over again. Everyone gathered around the crying girl, and Leah pushed her way through the circle and knelt down beside her. "What is wrong?" she asked.

"They have cut off the head of John the Baptist, and they have it in there!" Sarah let out a scream and dropped to the floor. A servant standing near the door opened it a crack and looked in. He quickly closed the door and suddenly looked sick. "It's true!" he said, and put his head down between his knees.

In a little while, Sarah revived, and before she even got up from the floor she said to Leah. "I'm through! I don't work here any longer." Then she got up and ran from the room.

For several minutes Leah stood still, thinking. Where could she go? What could she do? But still the thing that Sarah had said was the only thing that made sense, so she said to those around her, "I don't work here any longer, either. The rest of you can do what you like." Instead of going to her room, she went to Sarah's and knocked at the door, but Sarah was crying and did not hear. Leah pushed the door open and went in. She sat down beside Sarah and said, "I quit, too. I could not walk into that banquet hall again, knowing that had happened there."

Sarah said flatly, "I'm leaving just as soon as I can get a hold of myself; I can't stay here any longer."

"Don't do that, Sarah," said Leah. "It is the middle of the night and you have no place to go. Wait until morning, and then we will go together."

"Where can we go?" asked Sarah. She had been so concerned with leaving that she had not considered any future plans.

'I think we should find the disciples of John and start from there," said

Leah. Good, sensible Leah. How Sarah loved her!

Sarah remembered that she had seen Alex baptized by John in the Jordan, and the confusion and emptiness of her heart now made her long all the more to see him again, at least to talk to him. This possibility made the decision to find the disciples seem right and reasonable.

Leah said, "We better find another place in the palace to sleep tonight. Someone may come looking for us, and I don't want to talk to anyone. We will leave at daybreak."

The sun was just rising when they began to leave the palace, carrying their meager possessions. A band of men was at the front gate, talking to the guards there. "We are the disciples of John the Baptist, and we have come to claim his body for burial." Without hesitation, the guards let them in, and one of them went with them to the dungeon. Sarah said to Leah, "I want to go with them and see him for the last time."

Leah grabbed her arm. "Don't go! You would never get that memory out of your mind. Remember him as you saw him when he was at his best, when he was preaching at the river. Remember your own private talks with him."

In a short time, the men returned bearing the body wrapped in broad strips of cloth. Without a word, Sarah and Leah joined them and passed through the gate. The guards made no move to stop them.

News of John's death had spread rapidly; and, as they went along, people who had been touched by his ministry joined in the procession. Sarah remembered the last funeral procession in which she had a part, the funeral of Herod. How different this was! There was no elaborate pomp, but there was genuine grief. There was no organization, no marching army, but there was a gathering of people who felt a spiritual kinship with John.

As they neared Jericho, a crowd of people from Jerusalem and from the north joined them until the following seemed as large as it had been when Sarah and Herodias had come to hear John. How vivid that memory was now! Sarah had to suppress the anger that overwhelmed her as she thought of Herodias and her treachery; this was not a time for anger or Herodias. This was John's time. Even the grief that was all so evident around her seemed different. If anything, it was grief tinged with hope, for the people who spoke, spoke of accomplishment, of mission, and of the Messiah.

John was buried in a cave near where he had preached. As it was being sealed, the crowd sang Psalms.

A great prophet was gone!

The crowd was large, and Sarah looked in vain for Alex. Now that the funeral was over, both Sarah and Leah had come to the end of their plans. "Now what?" Sarah asked Leah. "Where do we go now?"

"I really don't know," said Leah. "John's death has changed everything for us, hasn't it?"

"No!" said Sarah, becoming angry again. "It was Salome. When I saw her shadow on the wall after she danced at Philip's palace, I had a strange feeling that she would be trouble; now look what she has done to our lives. Our prophet is murdered. We are without work, without a place to stay. And none of this is our fault. Why should we suffer for the evil of others?"

"Don't feel sorry for yourself," said Leah. "There are many things in life we cannot explain. I will admit that what we have seen could shake a person's faith; how could such a thing happen to a man like John? It seems that evil has triumphed again. But," she said with building conviction, 'there is a God in Heaven, and I would rather be John in his grave than Herod on his throne. And I would not trade places with Herodias for all the money in the world!"

As they walked along talking, a man and his wife walking near them could not help overhearing part of their conversation. The woman drew closer and asked them, "Did I hear you say that you had no place to go? My husband, James, and I can provide room for you."

As she explained further, her friendly smile gave them boldness to share with her. "Yes," said Leah, "we are in need. Sarah and I worked in the palace of Herod where John was killed. Sarah spent long hours talking with John at night, and she has been devastated by the loss. We left the palace with the disciples who came for his body, and we are never going back! But now we have nowhere to go."

The woman's husband broke in and said, "Yes, you do have a place to go! You are coming home with us, and you can stay until you get something permanent."

James and his wife, Ruth, lived in Jericho. The last time Sarah and Leah had come to Jericho, they had come from Jerusalem. This time they came from the opposite direction. Their lives, too, were moving in an opposite direction. As they passed near the wreckage of the palace where they had been, James explained that a small army under a man called Elijah had burned it. "Elijah!" said Sarah. "Him again!" She would have been more shocked if she had known that her father had been part of his army then and was now a slave in Damascus.

Both Sarah and Leah felt a sense of relief when they arrived in the home of their gracious hosts. They were emotionally drained and physically weary. Ruth showed them the guest chamber, a small room on the roof of the house. As they climbed the narrow steps that led to the roof, Leah realized how tired she was, but Sarah's thoughts went back to the night she had climbed the ladder to the roof of her home in Ebba. So much had happened since that night!

They both expected to fall asleep immediately, but sleep would not come. Perhaps they were too exhausted. Perhaps it was the unfamiliar place, perhaps it was the turmoil caused by the events of the previous days, perhaps it was the uncertainty that faced both of them as they looked ahead. Instead of sleeping, they talked far into the night. Finally they both fell into a deep sleep.

When they awoke the next morning, the sun was streaming through the narrow windows of the room. It was evidently long past dawn, and these two women who were accustomed to working from dawn to dusk felt guilty and lazy to be found in bed so late. They could not shake the feeling that they should hurry to make up for lost time and get to work immediately. But there was no work to be done, no job waiting for them. This realization ruined the luxury of sleeping late, and some of the apprehension of the previous day returned.

Before leaving the roof, both of them found a quiet place; Sarah in one corner, Leah in another. Their morning prayers were filled with praise and thanksgiving; but more than that — urgent pleas for guidance and clear direction. After being assured that they were attuned to the will and ways of God, they descended the steps, ready to face the opportunities and challenges of the day. Sarah was saying to Leah, "I feel as though I am facing a new beginning in my life; it is certainly a new chapter. I wonder how many new beginnings one should have in life. I seem to have more than my share."

"May this be the best chapter of them all!" said Leah. "Let's both trust God for better days."

Ruth had heard them coming and met them at the door with the greeting. " 'This is the day that the Lord has made,' " To which Sarah and Leah responded in unison, " 'We will rejoice and be glad in it.' "

What a good way to begin, thought Sarah. How different was the atmosphere in this home from the atmosphere in the palace. This place was an oasis of peace.

21

During breakfast the next morning, they learned that James had been up at dawn to tend his groves of balsam trees. In friendly conversation, Ruth told of the precious ointments and salves they made, which, she said proudly, were prized all over the world. Ruth's pleasant humor and easy smile made her easy to like. As time went on, they all began sharing the more intimate details of their lives. Sarah mentioned that she had been hoping to find Alex in the gathering at the funeral of John the Baptist. Ruth's eyes widened, and she asked intently, "Do you mean the Greek young man?"

"Yes," said Sarah in surprise. "Do you know him?"

"Do you mean Alex the silversmith?" asked Ruth.

"Yes! Yes!" said Sarah excitedly. "And you are *the* Sarah?" asked Ruth, her face brightening.

"Yes, I am Sarah. Tell me! Tell me! Do you know him?"

"Indeed, I do know him," said Ruth. "He has been looking for you, and now the good hand of God has brought you to us!"

"How do you know he is looking for me?" asked Sarah. She was puzzled. She certainly wanted to believe he was looking for her, but how could Ruth know that?

"He came from Jerusalem and was looking for work," explained Ruth. "A shopkeeper told him that James had been there looking for workers. James didn't go there for that purpose, but he just happened to mention it. 'Just happened,' " she chuckled. "But now we can see it was not chance at all! Alex came to work for us, and my husband was very impressed with him. In fact, he said to me, 'I think I see a deep spiritual hunger in that man; I think God has brought him to us for a reason.' We talked with him at great length, and we asked him if he would like to come with us to hear John. He was anxious to do so because he was looking for someone who could show him the way to God."

"But how did you know about me?" asked Sarah, still puzzled.

"On the way to hear John, we talked, and he told us about you and how he had lost you, and how he had been searching for you. But the best part is this: When he heard John, he responded immediately. When John called for people to be baptized, he did not hesitate a minute."

"I know!" said Sarah excitedly. "I was there and I saw him! I was with that evil woman, Herodias, and I couldn't get to him."

"It's a good thing you didn't," said Ruth. "That woman was the cause of his problems. Salome acccused him of attacking her, and Herodias determined to throw him in prison. He barely escaped before the guards came. He fled Jerusalem and ended up here."

"Salome again!" said Sarah. "How much heartache she has caused us. But where is Alex now? I must see him!" She had heard enough of the story. The rest of it could wait.

"He left a few days ago," Ruth told her, and Sarah's heart fell. Would they be separated forever? Would it always be like this? "But I know where he went," said Ruth in a hurry. She had seen the disappointment on Sarah's face and wanted this piece of good news to save her further grief. She explained, "A man named Andrew was one of John's disciples, but when Jesus of Nazareth came, John told Andrew and the others to follow Him. Andrew has been here a number of times, and now we believe that Jesus of Nazareth is the Messiah. This is all new to Alex, and it took him longer to respond; but, when he heard that Jesus was preaching near the Jordan, he decided to go and see for himself. He should be home any day now."

Any day now! I can't wait for "any day now!" thought Sarah, *too many things have come between us already!* "Leah," she said, "will you go with me to find him?"

Ruth smiled at her eagerness. "I have a better idea," she said. "I'll get James and we will go together. We know the place by the river; and, of course, we would like to hear Jesus again."

As Ruth went to get her husband, Sarah said to Leah, "I don't know if I can stand all this excitement. Too many things are happening too fast."

Leah smiled, and, with a twinkle in her eye, said, "You are right. We ought to wait until next week before we look for Alex."

"No!" shouted Sarah. Then as Leah grinned, she realized that Leah was only teasing, and they both laughed together. But then she added seriously, "I have lost too much of my life already; I can't allow whole days to slip away."

"Yes, you are right," replied Leah. "I have a feeling that, at long last, your life has turned to the bright side. I believe you will get your share of happiness after all."

With that, Ruth and James came in, and Ruth slid into the conversation.

"Yes indeed! And after I get some food together, we will all start on your journey of happiness."

Although Sarah had been disappointed many times, this time she was filled with nothing but hope. A tightness around her mouth had begun to loosen, and her round, dark eyes were beginning to sparkle again.

As they walked along the road, the conversation turned to the preaching of John and the effect it had had on people and the expectations it brought for renewal in Israel. Sarah said, thoughtfully, "It seems to me that every time something good arises, it is cut off before it can bear fruit. I think back to the days when I entertained the notion that I could be part of the answer to Israel's deliverance. I think that I have grown up since then. Especially after talking with John, I have come to see that our problems are much deeper than I had thought. Even if we got rid of the Romans, many of our problems would still remain. John taught me that our problems are not political, but spiritual."

"And," added Ruth, "John knew that even he was not the answer to our needs. We heard him say that One was coming who was so great that John was not worthy to loose His sandals."

"And," said James, "we now know who that One is: He is Jesus of Nazareth of Galilee. We will take you to hear Him sometime soon, if you'd like. You will understand about whom John was talking when you hear this man teach."

They were so engrossed in their conversation that only Sarah noticed a small group of men coming toward them. In the group — there was no doubt about it — was Alex! She could tell, even though they were still some distance away. "Look!" cried Sarah, "There is Alex!" And Ruth confirmed it. "You're right; it is Alex."

Although Sarah was so excited about seeing him, now she lost her nerve. She said to Ruth urgently, "Please go and talk with him. What if he has changed his mind? What if he isn't looking for me anymore! Please go and talk with him."

Before Ruth could respond, James said, "You wait here; I'll go," and he hurried off. Eagerly they watched as he approached the group and went up to Alex. Although they were too far away to hear what was being said, they knew by Alex's reaction. As soon as he saw Sarah, he left the group and almost ran to meet her. Sarah wanted to run to meet him, too, to throw her arms around him and never let him go, but she could not — that would not be right. Instead, she stood still, and smiled.

In those few moments of conversation James had with Alex, he had obviously imparted vital information about Sarah's feelings, and Alex's immediate response conveyed the same information to Sarah. He didn't ask, "How are you?" or, "How did you find me?" or engage in any small talk. He took a long breath and said slowly and deliberately, "Sarah, now that I have found you, I will never let you go."

Sarah was overwhelmed, overjoyed. She did not know how to respond! Suddenly, she felt awkward in the presence of her companions, so, to lighten the moment, she turned to Leah, James, and Ruth and said, "You are witnesses; you heard what he said. If he tries to run away again later, you can catch him."

The journey back to Jericho seemed brief; it was so filled with animated conversation. There was so much to say, so much to catch up on, and it seemed like everything had to be said at once.

This time they took the main road to Jericho, the same road they had traveled when they had come to Herod's palace. There beside the road in a good position to attract the travelers who journeyed that way was a silversmith's shop. Now it belonged to Alex. He did not invite them to come in, although Sarah would have liked to see it; he did not want her attention to be diverted to other things. "Wait right here," he said to them, "I have something very special to show you." Then he disappeared into the shop, and soon he returned with a gift, which he placed in Sarah's hand. It took her breath away! It was a silver medallion, larger than a coin, intricately engraved with two grape vines, branches intertwined. The work was magnificent, but then Sarah noticed something: Below one vine was the letter *A* and below the other, the letter *S*.

Still wide-eyed, Sarah said to him, "Then you knew all along that God would bring us together."

Alex did not reply but simply smiled. The pendant had a silver chain, and as Alex slipped it around Sarah's neck, he said to the others solemnly, "Witness what I have done. This is the sign and seal that I want Sarah for my wife."

Sarah did not need to respond, her shy smile and bowed head was all the answer Alex needed. The next day Sarah was still walking on air; finally, at long last, things were working out. So she was a little apprehensive when Leah said to her, "Sarah, come down off that cloud; let me talk to you like a mother."

"Oh, please, Leah," said Sarah. "Please don't tell me that I cannot trust my heart. Please don't disapprove."

"Set your mind at ease," Leah replied quickly. "I do not want to diminish your joy one bit, but if I were your mother, would you expect me to remain silent?"

"No, of course not," Sarah conceded. "It's just that I don't want anything to come in the way of our plans, our happiness."

"That's the point," said Leah. "I just want you to be sure that your plans and your happiness coincide. You must realize that it would be so easy for you to overlook anything that seemed to be the least bit negative. This decision is too big to rush into. Don't let things move at such a speed that they are difficult to stop."

"I know that you are right," Sarah replied. "I know that I don't want to hear anything but approval, but can you blame me? I have waited so long."

"So it wouldn't hurt to wait a little longer — just to be sure," said Leah gently.

"*Wait*? That's the one word I don't want to hear. Wait? How long? For what?"

Leah smiled and laughed gently. "Don't be so serious, Sarah. I am not telling you to wait long; I am telling you to be sure. If this is not the will of God for you, I want you to be able to back out. Your happiness for the rest of your life hangs on this decision; you must be sure it is right."

"Don't you think it is right for me?" asked Sarah nervously.

"Yes, I do," said Leah. "But I'm not the one who will have to live with this decision. You are."

Sarah got up and embraced Leah. "Thank you for your advice; I will do my best to follow it."

The waiting was not long. Alex spent as much time as possible with Sarah — and with Leah and James and Ruth. It seemed like a family, a strange family since they were not related, but a happy family. No one was surprised when Ruth said, "I think we should have the wedding next week."

A wedding in Israel was not a private affair; it involved the whole circle of friends and neighbors. It was also a spiritual affair. Both the bride and groom spent the day before the wedding fasting and praying. This was to remind them that what they were about to do was symbolic of Jehovah's taking His bride, Israel, to Himself. The quiet, solemn preparation made the rejoicing that followed even more meaningful.

The home of James and Ruth was bursting with excitement. Ruth and Leah both felt like the mother of the bride, though James happily protested that he was not old enough to be the father of the bride, but he was happy to be called a friend, and he entered in fully.

When the evening of the wedding day arrived, Sarah was dressed in bridal garments, complete with veil. Ruth fussed over her until she looked just right; James tried to hurry them along. A circle of women led the way out of the house and down the road to Alex's home. As they went along, neighbors joined in and the procession grew larger. Some carried lamps on long poles, and some carried torches. As they neared Alex's house, they could hear music, and their arrival was greeted with shouts of joy and singing.

Alex and Sarah stood side by side as a rabbi said to Alex, "Take her according to the Law of Moses and of Israel." Then the bride and groom were crowned with garlands as the friends shouted and sang. Then Alex signed the solemn agreement, promising to work for, honor, keep, and care for his bride. After they had ceremonially washed their hands, a benediction was said and the marriage supper began. It was a joyful time with singing and music. After a time, there was a quiet moment when the bridal benediction was recited.

Alex and Sarah were finally united.

22

Benazra arose early and went out into his courtyard to greet the rising sun. As he did so, he said, " 'From the rising of the sun to the going down of the same, may the Lord's name be praised! Blessed be the name of the Lord!' " Morning prayers were an important part of his day, now that he was no longer in business. He had reluctantly admitted that he was getting too old to handle all the concerns of his business empire, and the men who had learned the business from him were more than happy to buy him out.

At first, he felt relief and a sense of freedom, but he also felt a kind of emptiness; he found it hard to fill his time with meaningful activity. Many of his friends in the Jewish community of Damascus had moved to Jerusalem, and he had considered this; but Damascus had been his home for so long that he had not been able to bring himself to leave.

Although he was more than his allotted "three score years and ten" and his pace had slowed considerably, he was still stocky and sturdy. He was as solid as an ancient olive tree. His leathered brown face had deep lines permanently carved by years of frowns and smiles. His curly, thick hair was dark brown with silver streaks, and his beard was gray. His dark eyes were still alert and friendly.

Today, as usual, he walked to the marketplace to talk with friends, and to sit in the sun — "just as an old man should . . . just as an old man should," he said quietly to himself. A good old friend called to him from across the street. "Benazra! How does the new day find you?" Benazra replied in a friendly way. There was nothing unusual about their exchange, but a man carrying some gardening tools over his shoulder stopped in his tracks, and looked intently at Benazra. He started to move on, then hesitated. His indecision attracted Benazra's attention, so he asked, "Friend, are you looking for me?"

The man replied, "I don't know; is your name Benazra?"

"Yes, it is," said Benazra. "And it has been my name for many years and many journeys."

"Are you . . . were you a merchant?" asked the man tentatively.

126

"For many years I was," replied Benazra. Now his interest was aroused. He looked closely at the man, trying to recall if he had been a customer in the past, but he did not recognize him and came to the conclusion that he had never seen him before. The man persisted, "Did you ever take a girl to Jerusalem?"

"Several times," replied Benazra.

The stranger then began to describe the girl and the situation that concerned him.

Now Benazra's eyes brightened. "Do you mean Sarah?" he asked.

"Yes, yes, Sarah!" the man replied. "Did you take her to Jerusalem?"

"I did," Benazra said, "why do you ask?"

Now the man was so excited that the words just tumbled out of him. "I am Sarah's father. I am Asher. All I ever learned about my daughter is that a trader from Damascus named Benazra took her to Jerusalem, and that Zadok, our town elder had seen her in Jericho; so you can understand why I responded as I did when I heard your name. I have never been able to find anyone else who could give me any other news."

"Then I have more good news for you," said Benazra. "I, myself, bought her freedom and started her on a life of her own. When I saw her last — some time ago now — she was doing fine."

"What a relief to hear that," said Asher. "How I would like to see her again; I'm afraid that will never be possible."

"Never say *never*," said Benazra undaunted. "All things are possible with God."

"But I am a slave here, and I see no hope for freedom," said Asher realistically. "Chances are I will never see Sarah or Jerusalem again."

"You are a slave here?" asked Benazra in surprise. "I thought you were a farmer in Galilee. What happened?"

"I was, but I was caught up in the fervor of that man who called himself Elijah and promised to deliver Israel from the Romans. I wish I had never seen that man! My life has been nothing but trouble since I left to follow him. Now my hopes are gone." He spoke with resignation. He did not weep; he had run out of tears long before this.

"Don't be too sure about that," said Benazra. "Perhaps God has made our paths cross, just like Sarah's and mine. I bought her freedom because she seemed to have so much potential. I didn't want her to be destroyed. Wouldn't it be in keeping with the mysterious ways of God that He permit me to purchase your freedom as well?"

Asher felt uneasy about this man, who was really a stranger, making such an offer. Sensing his hesitation, Benazra said, "Oh, don't worry about being indebted to me; I will never live long enough to spend all my money. Besides, there are ways in which you can be of real help to me." Asher looked skeptical. Benazra continued, "I would like to see Jerusalem once again, and I would like to see Sarah again. I would especially like to see her face if I could meet her with you by my side! She will think that I am an angel from God." He laughed. "Yes, we can help each other to Jerusalem and search for Sarah together."

"But my master, Ramas . . ." said Asher.

"Ramas? Ramas? Ha! I could buy everything he owns and still have money left over," said Benazra. "Don't worry about him. Here, help me up, and we will go to see him right now."

As Benazra brushed the dust from his robe, Asher hesitated, thinking. A hasty decision had ruined his life before; he did not want to make another now. "Maybe you ought to wait and think this over," he said to Benazra. "He could ask for a great deal of money, and I would never be able to pay it back. Are you sure you want to do this?"

He was in turmoil. There was nothing in the world that he wanted more than his freedom and the chance to see Sarah again. But he had nothing to offer in return, no way to pay back Benazra. To take such a gift! *No,* he thought, *I had better turn it down; there must be come catch to it.*

"Come on," said Benazra, "I know what you are thinking. If the tables were turned — if you had the money and I was the slave, what would you do?"

"I'm not sure," confessed Asher. "I'm afraid I have come to the place where I have to look out for myself and not care about others. I am sorry to say that, but I think it is true. Besides, I think I would find it easier to give if I had it; it is hard for me to take what I haven't worked for." Benazra began walking away, still looking at Asher and listening attentively, coaxing him to walk while they discussed the matter.

The conversation had still not come to a conclusion by the time they arrived at the home of Ramas, but Benazra was not waiting for a conclusion; he had already decided what he would do. He simply said to Asher, "Wait here while I go in and talk with him."

"But . . ." said Asher.

Benazra did not wait for further talk; he went in.

After the greetings, Benazra told Ramas, "I would like to buy your slave, Asher." Ramas took only a moment to size up the situation. He sensed that he had the advantage over the old trader, and he intended to make the most of it; so he said shrewdly, "He's not for sale; he's a good gardener and I need him."

"Come, come, neighbor," said Benazra. "I know you don't need him; you only bought him because slaves were so cheap after the Romans defeated Sappo. You paid very little for him, and already you have gotten your money's worth many times over. You ought to let him go for nothing."

"For nothing?" ridiculed Ramus. "Nobody lets a good worker go for nothing! He knows his job and does it. It would cost me money to replace him."

"You have too many already, and they are costing you money to feed," said Benazra. "I will be doing you a favor to take him off your hands."

The bargaining went on like this for a long time; Benazra was in his element; it was a friendly contest, a battle of skills, but from the beginning they both knew that Benazra would not go home without Asher, and both knew that he would pay an inflated price. Finally the deal was struck; Benazra paid double what Asher was worth on the market. Ramus thought he had struck a clever deal. So did Benazra.

Benazra was happy for Asher's companionship, and as time progressed they became fast friends. Now he lived for one thing: He wanted to see Jerusalem again. For him the journey would be hard, but that did not matter. Asher would help him. "I want to go for the Feast of Tabernacles," he said. "That's the best feast of all." Benazra was not alone in that opinion. It was the most joyful feast, coming as it did after harvest. Because the weather was likely to be better for traveling in the autumn, this was the feast that attracted many foreign visitors, even more than Passover.

The city of Jerusalem would be overcrowded, but that didn't bother Benazra. "My old friend Simon will make room for us," he told Asher. As a matter of fact, everybody in Jerusalem would make room — on housetops, in courtyards, in the fields. Everywhere booths would be erected of branches to remind the people of the journey from Egypt to the land of promise when they had no permanent home.

Benazra made arrangements with the men who had taken over his caravan business, and they planned a trip from Damascus to Jerusalem at that time so they would give company and protection. He also bought a strong and sturdy donkey for the trip. He was filled with great anticipation; but, naturally, Asher was even more excited. He looked forward eagerly to renewing his vows at the Temple, almost like a lost sheep coming home, and he knew that now there was a possibility of finding Sarah again.

They took the direct trade route along the Jordan, crossing at Jericho. Not many people were in Jericho as they passed through; many had already left for the feast. As they passed a silversmith's shop that was closed, Benazra, still thinking as a business man, remarked, "That fellow should keep his shop open. Look at all the pilgrims passing by. He could do a booming business." He had no idea who owned the shop.

When they arrived at Jerusalem, they went directly to Simon's house. Simon joyfully embraced Benazra and said, "My old friend, I never thought I would see you again. You did well to come to Jerusalem again. This will bring joy to your life."

"And this is Asher, Sarah's father," said Benazra, introducing them.

Simon greeted him. "I haven't seen your daughter for a long time. Will she be coming to the feast?"

"I don't know, but I hope so," replied Asher.

"So do I," responded Benazra.

23

Alex had a humble house behind his shop. In a short time, Sarah had transformed this into a bright, cheerful home, and already she felt more than repaid for all the troubles she had endured in her life. Since happiness had been deferred so long, it seemed all the more sweet.

Leah stayed with James and Ruth, and they were happy to have her company. There was plenty of work to go around, and the industrious lady was a great help to them. Although they urged her to consider it her permanent home, she still felt like a guest. She didn't want to overstay her welcome; but for now since she saw no other option, she stayed on. Alex and Sarah were very frequent visitors, and Leah did not want to leave this warm circle of friends.

One night when they were all sitting together after the evening meal, James suggested, "Let's all go together to the Feast of Tabernacles this year. Who has more to thank the Lord for than we do?" So plans were made there and then to go up to Jerusalem, especially to celebrate the joy that had come to Alex and Sarah. Before Alex had met John the Baptist he had been an outsider; but, by his baptism, he had made his commitment to the God of Israel. Now he wanted to learn all he could about the feasts and customs, and with Sarah at his side, this was a double enjoyment. When the time came, they joined the procession that made its way to the Holy City.

The Temple was a magnificent sight, its marble, gold, and cedar glowing in the slanting rays of the late afternoon sun. The throng that filled the Temple grounds was huge, but they responded as one to the chants of the Hallel and thrilled to the sounds of the priests' silver trumpets. This was what gave Israel its national identity. Here they were, rich and poor, the noble and the lowly, people from the cities and villages of Israel, and Jews from Persia, India, Spain, Italy, and even Britain; but, as they sang their praise, they were one, one nation, one family.

The first night of the feast was the most spectacular. The Temple and its surroundings were lit by torches and giant candelabras, and the illumination would continue until the light of the rising sun took over the task. A festive atmosphere continued throughout the night with music, singing, and dancing.

The priests greeted the rising sun with blasts of their silver trumpets as they climbed the steps to the Court of the Women and proceeded to the Beautiful Gate.

Alex was overcome. There was a majesty and a joy about the celebration, a sense of community and fellowship that he had never experienced. Now he felt a part of it all. His eyes shone as he looked around at all the people, so many, so different, and he felt a part of them all. His handsome, bright smile was no longer unusual.

Then he saw a familiar face. He wasn't sure, but he thought he recognized the old man making his way through the crowd. He looked again, and still was not sure, so he said to Sarah, "That old man there . . . isn't that Benazra?"

"Where?" asked Sarah. "It's so hard to see with all the people milling around."

"Over there," said Alex. "I'm sure it is. Here, come with me. Let's catch up with him before he gets away."

After they had gone a few steps, Sarah caught sight of him, and then she noticed the man with him. Years had passed . . . she couldn't be sure. "Benazra! Benazra!" she called and started to run, not taking the time to excuse herself as she bumped her way through the people. Benazra heard his name called; he stopped, and when he turned, he saw Sarah running toward him. "Blessed be the God of Israel!" he exclaimed with joy. Then, turning to Asher at his side, he shouted, "Asher, here is your daughter!" Then Sarah was sure . . . she knew!

For a long time Alex could only stand on the sidelines as a happy witness. The reunion was a mixture of tears and hugs and laughter. "Oh, father . . . oh, Benazra," Sarah said over and over again. By the time she got around to introducing her new husband to her father, Leah, James, and Ruth had joined them. People who had no idea of what was happening watched and smiled. Sarah was saying, "My life is filled with so much happiness that I don't think I can contain it all." This was indeed, the Feast of Thanksgiving.

The rest of the feast days sped by quickly. There was so much to share. Each one had a story to tell; each contributed a part to the mosaic. When it seemed that all had been told, someone would remember another part, and a new color would be added to the pattern. For each, the unknown years were filled in until the whole past became a completed picture.

When the feast was over, people began their journeys, some of them very long, homeward. Most of them were part of large groups, talking and sharing as they went, keeping the spirit of the feast alive as they traveled.

Benazra and Asher were planning to spend the night in Jericho and leave the following day. They did not want to wait until all the other pilgrims were gone; they did not want to travel alone.

They had just passed through the gate leaving Jerusalem when Benazra called out, "Wait! Stop right here!" When he turned around, Sarah thought, *How touching! He knows he will probably never make another trip and wants to gaze at the Holy City one more time.* To everyone's surprise, he announced firmly, "I'm not going back to Damascus: Why should I? I have no business there. I have been away from Jerusalem too long already. I'm going to stay here; I'm going to attend every feast. No! more than that . . . I'm going to go up to the Temple every day to pray."

"What?" Sarah asked in surprise. "that may be a good idea, Benazra, but you ought to think this through. You might regret a hasty decision."

"At my age, hasty decisions are the only kind I have time for," laughed Benazra. Sarah was about to continue arguing with him about his abrupt change of plans; but, when she reconsidered, she could understand his longings. Before anyone had a further opportunity to dissuade him, he turned to Asher and said, "Stay with me! You will be a son to me, and I don't want to stay alone. I will buy a house here, and when I go to sleep with my fathers and my bones are laid to rest near the Holy City, the house will be yours. What do you say, Asher?" Then he added with a twinkle in his eye, "You owe me this favor!"

Asher was sure that Benazra had silently thought through this decision, but he tried to slow down the rapid pace of the changes around him, so he asked, "What about your house and all your things in Damascus? What will you do about them?"

"There's nothing there that I really care about anymore," said Benazra. "One of these days when my old caravan passes through, I will send you back to settle up things. But I don't need to go back again. I belong here."

Asher hesitated, and Benazra thought he might say no, but he was hesitating for another reason. He had been considering his own serious decision. Now that things were pushing him, he could delay no longer.

"I will," he said, "if Leah will stay with me and be my wife."

Sarah was so taken by surprise that she looked at her father, wide-eyed, and shouted, "What?"

Leah was the only one who was not surprised. Of course, Asher had said nothing — nothing verbally, that is — but she had read it in his eyes. She knew that he had been struggling for days to get up the courage to declare himself. She thought of helping him, but decided it would be best for him to take this big step on his own. She had no doubt that she would have a good life with him, and she knew she would fill the void for him. Her only fear was that he would return to Damascus before he gained the courage to say something.

"That's a wonderful idea!" said Benazra. "I will have both a son and a daughter to brighten my old age." Then he added with a sly smile, "I will also be getting a good cook. That's important, too." And they all laughed together.

Asher took Leah's hand and asked, "What do you say, Leah, will you?"

Leah's whole face glowed as she said quietly, "Yes, I will."

"Do you know what?" said Sarah as she hugged Leah. "That will really make you my mother!"

This was a surprising turn of events, but everyone seemed to benefit greatly from the outcome. It was hard to say who rejoiced the most. Benazra had obtained his heart's desire to be in the Holy City, near the Temple, and now he had a son and daughter. Sarah had her father again and would see him often; she also had gained a mother. Leah had gotten not only a husband, but a family as well, and her future was finally secure. Alex gained a share in them all!

"Well, Benazra," said Ruth when the excitement had died down, "you are going to have to leave Jerusalem after all; you wouldn't want to miss the wedding, would you? This time, it will be in our house."

How they rejoiced as they resumed their journey. This was one of many feasts that they would attend. When they finally quieted down, Sarah said, "God's ways are sometimes mysterious, but He always cares for His own."

To this they all said, "Amen."